# PRIMARY MATHEMATICS

## TEXTBOOK 5A

**Common Core** Edition

SINGAPORE MATH® PROGRAM

**Marshall Cavendish**
Education

US Distributor

SM Singapore Math Inc.®

BLANK

Original edition published under the title Primary Mathematics Textbook 5A
© 1981 Curriculum Planning & Development Division, Ministry of Education, Singapore
Published by Times Media Private Limited

This edition © 2014 Marshall Cavendish Education Pte Ltd

**Published by Marshall Cavendish Education**
Times Centre, 1 New Industrial Road, Singapore 536196
Customer Service Hotline: (65) 6213 9444
US Office Tel: (1-914) 332 8888 | Fax: (1-914) 332 8882
E-mail: tmesales@mceducation.com
Website: www.mceducation.com

Distributed by
**Singapore Math Inc.®**
19535 SW 129th Avenue
Tualatin, OR 97062, U.S.A.
Tel:  (503) 557 8100
Website: www.singaporemath.com

First published 2014
Reprinted 2014, 2015, 2016

*Primary Mathematics (Common Core Edition) Textbook 5A*
ISBN 978-981-01-9837-4

Printed in Malaysia

Primary Mathematics (Common Core Edition) is adapted from Primary Mathematics Textbook 5A (3rd Edition), originally
developed by the Ministry of Education, Singapore. This edition contains new content developed by Marshall Cavendish
Education Pte Ltd, which is not attributable to the Ministry of Education, Singapore.

We would like to acknowledge the contributions by:

**The Project Team from the Ministry of Education, Singapore that developed the original Singapore edition**
Project Director: Dr Kho Tek Hong
Team Members: Hector Chee Kum Hoong, Liang Hin Hoon, Lim Eng Tann, Ng Siew Lee, Rosalind Lim Hui Cheng,
Ng Hwee Wan

**Primary Mathematics (Common Core Edition)**
Richard Askey, Emeritus Professor of Mathematics from University of Wisconsin, Madison
Jennifer Kempe, Curriculum Advisor from Singapore Math Inc.®

# PREFACE

**PRIMARY MATHEMATICS** Common Core Edition is a complete program from Marshall Cavendish Education, the publisher of Singapore's successful *Primary Mathematics* series. Newly adapted to align with the Common Core State Standards for mathematics, the program aims to equip students with sound concept development, critical thinking and efficient problem-solving skills.

**Mathematical concepts** are introduced in the opening pages and taught to mastery through specific learning tasks that allow for immediate assessment and consolidation.

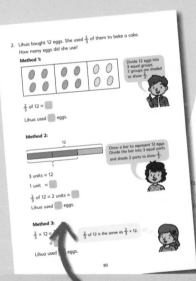

The **modeling method** enables students to visualize and solve mathematical problems quickly and efficiently.

**The Concrete → Pictorial → Abstract** approach enables students to encounter math in a meaningful way and translate mathematical skills from the concrete to the abstract.

The **pencil icon** ✏️ Exercise 2, pages 18-20 provides quick and easy reference from the Textbook to the relevant Workbook pages. The **direct correlation** of the Workbook to the Textbook facilitates focused review and evaluation.

New mathematical concepts are introduced through a **spiral progression** that builds on concepts already taught and mastered.

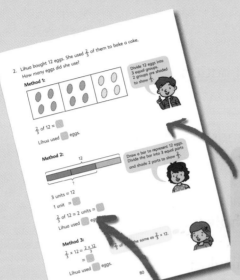

**Metacognition** is employed as a strategy for learners to monitor their thinking processes in problem solving. Speech and thought bubbles provide guidance through the thought processes, making even the most challenging problems accessible to students.

The color patch is used to invite active student participation and to facilitate lively discussion about the mathematical concepts taught.

Regular **reviews** in the Textbook provide consolidation of concepts learned.

The **glossary** effectively combines pictorial representation with simple mathematical definitions to provide a comprehensive reference guide for students.

# CONTENTS

# 1 WHOLE NUMBERS

## 1 Large Numbers

On September 1, 2006, the population of the world was 6,541,161,782.

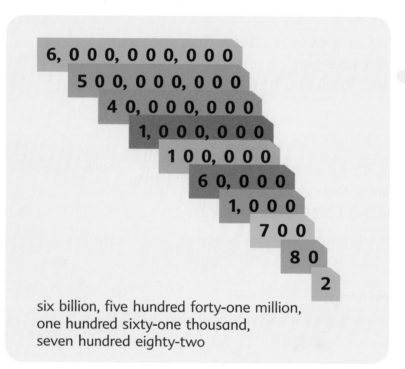

6, 0 0 0, 0 0 0, 0 0 0
500, 0 0 0, 0 0 0
40, 0 0 0, 0 0 0
1, 0 0 0, 0 0 0
100, 0 0 0
60, 0 0 0
1, 0 0 0
7 0 0
8 0
2

six billion, five hundred forty-one million,
one hundred sixty-one thousand,
seven hundred eighty-two

6, 5 4 1, 1 6 1, 7 8 2

| Billions | | | Millions | | | Thousands | | | Ones | | |
|---|---|---|---|---|---|---|---|---|---|---|---|
| Hundreds | Tens | Ones | Hundreds | Tens | Ones | Hundreds | Tens | Ones | Hundreds | Tens | Ones |
| | | 6 | 5 | 4 | 1 | 1 | 6 | 1 | 7 | 8 | 2 |

Standard form: 6,541,161,782

Expanded form:

6,000,000,000 + 500,000,000 + 40,000,000 + 1,000,000 +
100,000 + 60,000 + 1,000 + 700 + 80 + 2

Starting from the right, each group of 3 digits forms a **period**.
Commas separate the periods.

The value of the digit 5 in 6,541,161,782 is 500,000,000.
It is in the hundred-millions place.

The value of the digit 4 in 6,541,161,782 is 40,000,000.
It is in the ten-millions place.

6,541,161,782 = ⬜ + 1,782

1. Write the following numbers in words and in expanded form.
   (a) 340,600
   (b) 50,493,400
   (c) 34,034,005,182

2. The maximum distance from the sun to Uranus is about
   two billion, eight hundred seventy million kilometers.
   Write this number in figures.

3. (a) 3,000,000 + 400 + 4 = ⬜

   (b) 60 + 1,000,000 + 5,000 + 20,000,000 + 4 = ⬜

4. A house on a lake sold for $2,348,564.

   (a) Write the number in words and in expanded form.

   (b) The digit 5 is in the ☐ place.

   (c) 2,348,564 = 2,348,500 + ☐

   There are 23,485 hundreds in 2,348,564.

   (d) The digit ☐ is in the thousands place.

   2,348,564 = ☐ + 564

   There are ☐ thousands in 2,348,564.

   (e) There are ☐ ten thousands in 2,348,564.

   (f) There are ☐ hundred thousands in 2,348,564.

5. On July 1, 2006, the population of the United States was 295,734,134.

   (a) Write the number in words.
   (b) How many ones are in 295,734,134?

   (c) 295,734,134 is ☐ more than 734,134.

   There are ☐ millions in 295,734,134.

   (d) What digit is in the ten millions place?
   (e) How many ten millions are in 295,724,124?

6. Find the value of each of the following.

   (a) Ten thousand more than 345,045,000 is ☐.

   (b) Ten million less than 2,934,300,200 is ☐.

   (c) ☐ is one hundred less than 10,000,000.

   (d) ☐ is one hundred thousand more than 4,992,000.

7. The land area of the United States is 9,161,923 square kilometers.
   The land area of China is 9,326,410 square kilometers.
   Which country has more land area?

9,161,923
9,326,410

> Starting from the left, compare the digits in each place value, until 2 digits are different.

8. Which number is smaller, 385,400,302 or 85,329,400?

9. Copy and write >, <, or = in each ◯.

   (a)  4,513,452 ◯ 4,513,452

   (b)  24,602,000,000 ◯ 26,402,000

10. Arrange the numbers in increasing order.
    (a)  345,453,435   435,453,345   453,435,345   354,345,543
    (b)  26,934,000   6,293,400   239,693,000   36,349,000

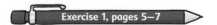
Exercise 1, pages 5—7

# ② Approximation and Estimation

In 2005, 32,641,526 people attended the NCAA football games.

Carla **rounds** 32,641,526 to the nearest million.

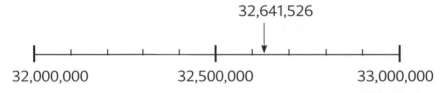

32,641,526 ≈ 33,000,000

32,641,526 is **approximately** 33,000,000.

There were about 33 million people.

Willie rounds 32,641,526 to the nearest ten million.

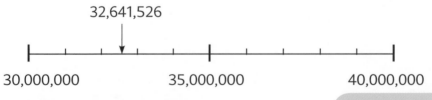

32,641,526 ≈ 30,000,000

32,641,526 is **approximately** 30,000,000.

There were about 30 million people.

1. In 2005, attendance for the Wimbledon Tennis Championship was 467,188.
   Round the number to the nearest thousand.

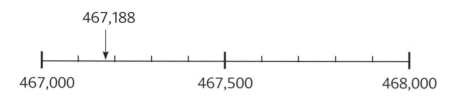

467,188 ≈ ◻

   Round each number to the nearest thousand.
   (a)  60,400
   (b)  179,500
   (c)  999,900

2. Round 2,750,000 to the nearest hundred thousand.

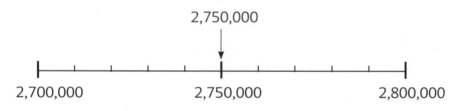

2,750,000 ≈ ◻

2,750,000 is exactly halfway between 2,700,000 and 2,800,000. **Take 2,800,000 as the nearest hundred thousand.**

3. Round 172,866,529 to the nearest million.

What digit is in the millions place?

$\downarrow$

1 7 2, 8 6 6, 5 2 9

What digit is in the next lower place?

$\downarrow$

1 7 2, 8 6 6, 5 2 9

Do we round up or down?

172,866,529 is ☐ rounded to the nearest million.

> To round a number, we look at the digit in the next lower place value. If it is less than 5, we round down. If it is 5 or greater, we round up.

4. Round each number to the place named.
   (a) 285,043 : ten thousands
   (b) 25,590,430 : millions
   (c) 5,996,450,012 : hundred millions

5. Round 4,569,325 to the place named.
   (a) tens
   (b) hundreds
   (c) thousands
   (d) ten thousands
   (e) hundred thousands
   (f) millions

Exercise 2, page 8

6. Find the value of 180,000 ÷ 3.

180,000 ÷ 3 = ☐

180 thousands ÷ 3 = 60 thousands

7. Find the value of each of the following.
   (a) 2,700,000 + 600,000
   (b) 4,500,000 − 800,000
   (c) 700,000 × 4
   (d) 350,000 ÷ 5

8. Estimate the value of each of the following.
   (a) 32,370 + 4,959
   (b) 24,890 + 5,016
   (c) 48,207 − 9,864
   (d) 54,500 − 6,892
   (e) 639,043 + 599,216
   (f) 7,812,300 + 896,900
   (g) 830,700 − 426,500
   (h) 4,562,718 − 732,491

9. Estimate the value of 293,400 × 6.

   293,400 × 6 ≈ 300,000 × 6

   = ☐

10. Estimate the value of 542,300 ÷ 8.

    542,300 ÷ 8 ≈ 560,000 ÷ 8

    = ☐

    480,000 and 560,000 are multiples of 8. Take 542,300 ≈ 560,000.

11. Estimate the value of each of the following.
    (a) 8,659 × 4
    (b) 6,023 × 9
    (c) 7,080 ÷ 8
    (d) 4,378 ÷ 7

12. Estimate the value of each of the following.
    (a) 380,600 × 9
    (b) 979,400 × 5
    (c) 478,500 ÷ 6
    (d) 378,200 ÷ 4

Exercise 3, pages 9—11

# 3 Factors and Multiples

Adam has 18 stamps. He arranges the stamps in sets of 3.

$$18 = 3 \times 6$$

3 is a **factor** of 18.

18 is a **multiple** of 3.

$$\begin{array}{r} 6 \\ 3\overline{)18} \\ \underline{18} \\ 0 \end{array}$$

18 can be divided by 3 exactly.

Is 18 a **multiple** of 6?

Is 6 a **factor** of 18?

1. List the first 12 multiples of 5.

5, 10, 15, 20, ...

2. Is 4 a factor of 110?

```
      2 7
  4 ) 1 1 0
      8
    ─────
      3 0
      2 8
    ─────
        2
```

Since 110 cannot be divided by 4 exactly, 4 is not a factor of 110.

3. Which of the following numbers have 2 as a factor?
   (a)  42                           (b)  63
   (c)  128                          (d)  349

Remember:
2 is a factor of all even numbers.

4. Which of the following numbers have 3 as a factor?
   (a)  92                           (b)  69
   (c)  252                          (d)  413

3 is a factor of a number if the sum of its digits is a multiple of 3.

5. Which of the following numbers have 5 as a factor?
   (a)  40                           (b)  82
   (c)  195                          (d)  660

5 is a factor of a number if the last digit is 0 or 5.

6. Find the factors of 84.

$$84 = 1 \times 84$$
$$= 2 \times 42$$
$$= 3 \times 28$$
$$= ...$$

7. Find the factors of each number.
   (a)  36          (b)  64          (c)  56          (d)  72
   (e)  124         (f)  144         (g)  108         (h)  120

8. List the common factors of 12 and 20. What is the **greatest common factor** of 12 and 20?
   Factors of 12 : 1, 2, 3, 4, 6, 12
   Factors of 20 : 1, 2, 4, 5, 10, 20

1, 2 and 4 are common factors of 12 and 20. 4 is the **greatest common factor** of 12 and 20.

9. What is the greatest common factor of the following numbers?
   (a) 9 and 21
   (b) 12 and 18
   (c) 12, 36, and 42

10. Is 48 a common multiple of 6 and 8?

11. Give a common multiple of 3, 4 and 9.

12. Give a common multiple of 5 and 8.
    Multiples of 5 : 5, 10, 15, 20, 25, 30, 35, **40** ...
    Multiples of 8 : 8, 16, 24, 32, **40** ...

40 is a common multiple of 5 and 8. It is also the **lowest common multiple** of 5 and 8.

13. What is the lowest common multiple of the following numbers?
    (a) 3 and 4
    (b) 6 and 9
    (c) 4, 5, and 6

Exercise 4, pages 12–14

## 4 Prime Factorization

Find all the prime numbers to 50.

First, list the numbers from 1 to 50:

| 1 | 2 | 3 | 4 | 5 | 6 | 7 | 8 | 9 | 10 |
|---|---|---|---|---|---|---|---|---|----|
| 11 | 12 | 13 | 14 | 15 | 16 | 17 | 18 | 19 | 20 |
| 21 | 22 | 23 | 24 | 25 | 26 | 27 | 28 | 29 | 30 |
| 31 | 32 | 33 | 34 | 35 | 36 | 37 | 38 | 39 | 40 |
| 41 | 42 | 43 | 44 | 45 | 46 | 47 | 48 | 49 | 50 |

A **prime number** is a number greater than 1. It has exactly two factors, 1 and the number itself.

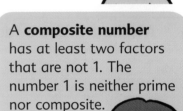

Cross out 1, since it is not a prime number.

Except for 2 itself, cross out all the remaining numbers that have 2 as a factor.

Except for 3 itself, cross out all the remaining numbers that have 3 as a factor.

A **composite number** has at least two factors that are not 1. The number 1 is neither prime nor composite.

Why do we not have to cross out numbers that have 4 as a factor?

Except for 5 itself, cross out all the remaining numbers that have 5 as a factor.

Why do we not have to cross out numbers that have 6 as a factor?

Except for 7 itself, cross out all the remaining numbers that have 7 as a factor.

Why can we stop after crossing out numbers that have 7 as a factor?

List the numbers to 50 that have not been crossed out. These are the prime numbers less than 50.

What do you notice about the ones digits of these prime numbers?

There are some pairs of prime numbers whose difference is two. These are called twin primes. 3 and 5 are twin primes. List all the twin primes less than 50.

1. The factors of 12 are 1, 2, 3, 4, 6 and 12. Which factors of 12 are prime factors?

> **Prime factors** are any factors of a number which are prime numbers.

2. Express 12 as a product of prime factors only.

   12 = ⬜ × ⬜ × ⬜

3. Find the prime factorization of 72.

> **Prime factorization** is the process of factoring a composite number into its prime factors.

**Method 1**: Use a factor tree.

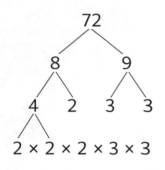

2 × 2 × 2 × 3 × 3

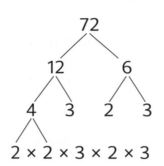

2 × 2 × 3 × 2 × 3

**Method 2**: Use continuous division, starting with the lowest prime number that is a factor.

```
2 | 72
2 | 36
2 | 18
3 | 9
3 | 3
  | 1
```

72 = 2 × 2 × 2 × 3 × 3

4. Find the prime factorization of the following numbers.
   (a) 15
   (b) 50
   (c) 36

Exercise 5, page 15

5. (a) $2^4$ is read as **2 to the fourth power**. What is its value?

$$2^4 = 2 \times 2 \times 2 \times 2 = \boxed{\phantom{00}}$$

(b) Find the value of 4 to the third power.

$$4^3 = 4 \times 4 \times 4 = \boxed{\phantom{00}}$$

(c) Find the value of 10 to the sixth power.

$$10^6 = 10 \times 10 \times 10 \times 10 \times 10 \times 10 = \boxed{\phantom{00}}$$

$2^3 = 2 \times 2 \times 2$

$2^3$ ←exponent

base

The exponent tells us how many times the base is used as a factor.

6. Find the value of each of the following.
   (a) $3^3$  (b) $7^2$
   (c) $3^3 \times 7^2$  (d) $1^7$
   (e) $10^3$  (f) $10^1$

7. Rewrite each of the following using exponents.
   (a) $2 \times 2 \times 2 \times 5 \times 5 \times 5$
   (b) $5 \times 3 \times 3 \times 5 \times 7$
   (c) $11 \times 7 \times 11 \times 7$
   (d) $3 \times 2 \times 10 \times 10 \times 10 \times 10 \times 10$

8. Find the value of each of the following.
   (a) $8 \times 10^4$
   (b) $32 \times 10^6$
   (c) $806 \times 10^7$

9. Show the prime factorization of 72 using exponents. Start with the lowest prime number.

$$72 = 2 \times 2 \times 2 \times 3 \times 3 = 2^3 \times 3^2$$

10. Show the prime factorization of each of the following using exponents.
    (a) 60  (b) 24
    (c) 100  (d) 82

Exercise 6, pages 16–17

# 5 Multiplying by Tens, Hundreds, or Thousands

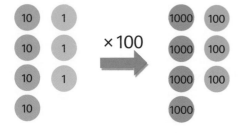

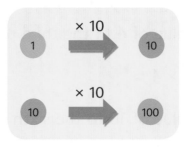

$43 \times 10 = 430$

$43 \times 10^1 = 430$

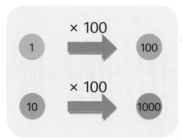

$43 \times 100 = 4{,}300$

$43 \times 10^2 = 4{,}300$

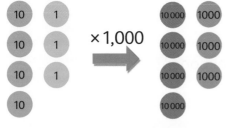

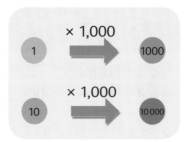

$43 \times 1{,}000 = 43{,}000$

$43 \times 10^3 = 43{,}000$

1. Multiply.
   (a) $3,280 \times 10$
   (b) $100 \times 53,600$
   (c) $630 \times 10^3$

2. Multiply 16 by 700.

   $16 \times 700 = 16 \times 7 \times 100$
   $= 112 \times 100$
   $= 11,200$

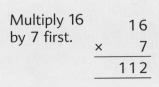

Multiply 16 by 7 first.

$$\begin{array}{r} 16 \\ \times \quad 7 \\ \hline 112 \end{array}$$

3. Multiply 485 by 3.
   Then find the value of each of the following.
   (a) $485 \times 30$
   (b) $485 \times 300$
   (c) $485 \times 3 \times 10^3$

4. Multiply 45,000 by 6.
   Then find the value of each of the following.
   (a) $45,000 \times 60$
   (b) $45,000 \times 600$
   (c) $45,000 \times 6,000$

5. Multiply.
   (a) $200 \times 5,000$
   (b) $600 \times 9,000$
   (c) $800 \times 60,000$
   (d) $500 \times 20,000$
   (e) $40,000 \times 600$
   (f) $2,000 \times 500,000$

6. Estimate the value of $70,200 \times 190$.

   $70,200 \times 190 \approx 70,000 \times 200$

   $= $

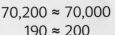

$70,200 \approx 70,000$
$190 \approx 200$

7. Mrs. Bates needs 543 costumes for
   her students to take part in a parade.
   Each costume costs $35. Give a quick
   estimate of the total cost of the costumes.

   $35 \times 543 \approx 40 \times 500$
   $= 20,000$

   The total cost is about $20,000.

8. Estimate the value of each of the following.
   (a) $529 \times 340$
   (b) $7,500 \times 386$
   (c) $7,804 \times 590$

Exercise 7, pages 18–20

# 6 Dividing by Tens, Hundreds, or Thousands

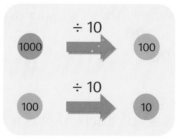

$$2,300 \div 10 = 230$$
$$2,300 \div 10^1 = 230$$

$$2,300 \div 100 = 23$$
$$2,300 \div 10^2 = 23$$

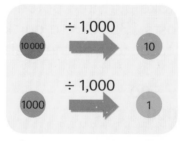

$$23,000 \div 1,000 = 23$$
$$23,000 \div 10^3 = 23$$

1. Divide.
   (a) 5,200 ÷ 10      (b) 74,000 ÷ 100      (c) 4,000,000 ÷ $10^3$

2. (a) Divide 15,000 by 30.

   15,00**0** ÷ 3**0** = 15,00**0** ÷ 1**0** ÷ 3
   = 1,500 ÷ 3
   = 500

   15,000 ÷ 30

   (b) Divide 15,000 by 300.

   15,0**00** ÷ 3**00** = 15,0**00** ÷ 1**00** ÷ 3
   = 150 ÷ 3
   = 50

   15,000 ÷ 300

   (c) Divide 15,000 by 3,000.

   15,**000** ÷ 3,**000** = 15,**000** ÷ 1,**000** ÷ 3
   = 15 ÷ 3
   = 5

   15,000 ÷ 3,000

3. Divide.
   (a) 2,800 ÷ 40      (b) 640,000 ÷ 800      (c) 20,000,000 ÷ 5,000

4. Estimate the value of 29,920 ÷ 380.
   29,920 ÷ 380 ≈ 28,000 ÷ 400
   =

   29,920 ≈ 28,000
   380 ≈ 400

5. Maria paid $959 for 33 copies of a new software.
   Give a quick estimate of the cost per copy.
   959 ÷ 33 ≈ 900 ÷ 30
   = 30

   The cost per copy was about $30.

6. Estimate the value of each of the following.
   (a) 63,980 ÷ 81      (b) 22,050 ÷ 340      (c) 63,800 ÷ 6,700

Exercise 8, pages 21–24

1. Which one of the following numbers has the digit 6 in the ten thousands place?
   - (A) 6,541,000
   - (B) 640,059
   - (C) 546,109
   - (D) 5,164,000

2. A house is sold for about $2,400,000. Which one of the following could be the actual selling price of the house?
   - (A) $2,356,000
   - (B) $2,299,000
   - (C) $2,690,000
   - (D) $2,030,000

3. The factors of 24 are 1, 2, 3, 4, 6, 8, _____ and 24.
   - (A) 9
   - (B) 0
   - (C) 12
   - (D) 10

4. Select True or False.
   - (a) The first multiple of 6 is 12.                                    True / False
   - (b) 1,000 less than 20,000 is 19,000.                          True / False

5. Select True or False.
   - (a) The lowest common multiple of 8 and 12 is 24.     True / False
   - (b) The greatest common factor of 36 and 18 is 6.      True / False

6. (a) Write 8,574,932 in expanded form.

   (b) The digit 7 is in the ⬜ place.

   (c) The value of the digit 8 is ⬜.

7. Write in standard form.
   - (a) 368 thousands 7 hundreds
   - (b) 2 millions 732 thousands
   - (c) 74 billions 50 millions 4 ones
   - (d) Sixty-six hundred thousand, six hundred six

8. What is the missing number in each ⬜?

   (a) The digit 3 in 40,837,405 stands for 3 × ⬜.

   (b) The value of the digit 6 in 206,791,580 is ⬜.

9. What is the missing number?

    $95{,}087{,}000 = 90{,}000{,}000 + \boxed{\phantom{000}} + 80{,}000 + 7000$

10. Write the following in figures.
    (a) Five hundred fifteen thousand, four hundred seven
    (b) Four million, six hundred thousand

11. Write the following in words.
    (a) 4,500,000                    (b) 162,003
    (c) 872,520                      (d) 1,034,000

12. What is the value of the digit 9 in 9,364,000?

13. In 6,543,000, what is the digit in the ten thousands place?

14. Write a number less than one million that has 7 in both the hundred thousands place and the tens place.

15. How many millions are in 16,453,000?

16. How many hundred thousands are in 51,283,000?

17. (a) What number is one thousand less than one million?
    (b) What number is one hundred thousand less than one hundred million?

18. What is the missing number in each $\boxed{\phantom{0}}$ for this number pattern?

    $3{,}600{,}000,\ \boxed{\phantom{0}},\ 4{,}800{,}000,\ 5{,}400{,}000,\ \boxed{\phantom{0}}$

19. An airplane traveled a distance of 2,946 km. Round the distance to the nearest 1,000 km.

20. The population of Marina Town is 280,524. Round the number to the nearest 1,000.

21. Juan bought a car for $42,680. Round this amount of money to the nearest $1,000.

22. The air distance between Singapore and London is 10,873 km. Round this distance to the nearest 100 km.

23. (a)  Round $437,549 to the nearest $1,000.
    (b)  Round 42,652 km to the nearest 1,000 km.

24. Round off each number to the nearest 1,000.
    Then estimate the value of each of the following.
    (a)  3,472 + 1,607                 (b)  9,035 − 5,712
    (c)  29,074 + 5,872                (d)  14,236 − 6,223

25. Estimate the value of each of the following.
    (a)  3,268 × 7                      (b)  4,312 ÷ 6

26. What are the factors of 32?

27. What are the common factors of 30 and 45?

28. List the first six multiples of 7.

29. What is the smallest number that can be divided by 3, 6,
    and 8 exactly?

30. What is the sum of the first four multiples of 6?

31. What is the greatest common factor of 24 and 32?

32. What is the lowest common multiple of 8 and 10?

33. Find the sum of the prime numbers between 1 and 10.

34. Find the prime factorization of 68.

35. Find the value of $5^2 \times 7^2 \times 10^2$.

36. Copy and write >, < or = in each ⬤.

    (a)  $5^2$ ⬤ $5 \times 2$

    (b)  $3 \times 3 \times 2 \times 3 \times 7$ ⬤ $2 \times 3^4 \times 7$

    (c)  $4 \times 97$ ⬤ $(100 \times 4) - (3 \times 4)$

    (d)  $3^3 \times 7$ ⬤ $3 \times 3 \times 7$

37. Write the prime factorization of each of the following using exponents.
   (a) 96
   (b) 105
   (c) 120
   (d) 48
   (e) 117
   (f) 50
   (g) 72
   (h) 150
   (i) 350

38. Multiply or divide.
   (a) $1,245 \times 4,000$
   (b) $1,280 \div 80$
   (c) $84,000 \div 7,000$

39. Find the value of each of the following.
   (a) $670 \times 10$
   (b) $728 \times 10^2$
   (c) $350 \times 10^3$
   (d) $4,300 \div 10$
   (e) $58,000 \div 10^2$
   (f) $628,000 \div 10^3$

40. Estimate the value of each of the following.
   (a) $4,825 \times 63$
   (b) $7,134 \div 82$

41. Estimate the value of each of the following.
   (a) $381 \times 12$
   (b) $7,706 \times 220$
   (c) $5,106 \times 234$
   (d) $667 \times 4,850$
   (e) $6,250 \div 78$
   (f) $20,769 \div 36$
   (g) $382,700 \div 940$
   (h) $61,050 \div 730$

42. What is the smallest number that can be formed from the digits 7, 9, 0, 2, 6, and 5? All of the digits must be used.

43. Amy estimated the value of $345,459 + 89,120$ to be 400,000. Jonah estimated the value of $345,459 + 89,120$ to be 440,000. Who is correct? Why?

Review 1, pages 25—29

# 2 MORE CALCULATIONS WITH WHOLE NUMBERS

## 1 Order of Operations

Shelby collects glass figurines. She has 6 of them displayed on the mantelpiece and the rest of them displayed in a glass case with 4 shelves. Each shelf has 8 glass figurines. How many figurines does Shelby have?

$6 + 4 \times 8 = 6 + 32$

$$= \boxed{\phantom{00}}$$

Shelby has $\boxed{\phantom{0}}$ glass figurines.

> **Order of Operations:** Do multiplication or division from left to right, then addition or subtraction from left to right.

Briana collects postcards from the places she has visited. For each place she has visited, she collects 6 cards with scenic places on them and 4 with native animals. So far, she has collected cards from 8 places. How many postcards does Briana have?

Can we use the same expression we used for Shelby's collection?

To show that we want to add the total number of postcards from each place first, we use parentheses.

An expression has numbers and operation signs (+, −, ×, ÷) grouped together which can be computed as a number. It does not have an equal sign.

$(6 + 4) \times 8 = 10 \times 8$

$$= \boxed{\phantom{00}}$$

Briana has $\boxed{\phantom{0}}$ postcards.

Compute the expression in parentheses first.

1. Find the value of 7 + 4 + 5 + 3 + 8 + 6.

    7 + 4 + 5 + 3 + 8 + 6 = 20 + 5 + 8

    =

    If the expression has only addition, you can add in any order.

    7 + 4 + 5 + 3 + 8 + 6

2. Find the value of 50 × 28 × 2.

    50 × 28 × 2 = 100 × 28

    =

    If the expression has only multiplication, you can multiply in any order.

    50 × 28 × 2

3. Find the value of each of the following expressions.
    (a) 30 + 25 + 20
    (b) 8 + 5 + 75 + 20 + 25
    (c) 45 + 65 + 45 + 35
    (d) 35 + 30 + 15 + 70
    (e) 20 × 35 × 5
    (f) 86 × 25 × 4
    (g) 2 × 30 × 15
    (h) 8 × 4 × 240 × 2

4. Find the value of 160 ÷ 4 + 2 × 8 − 8.

    $\underline{160 \div 4} + 2 \times 8 - 8$

    = $40 + \underline{2 \times 8} - 8$

    = $\underline{40 + 16} - 8$

    = 56 − 8

    =

    If the expression has different kinds of operations, use the order of operations.

5. Find the value of 160 ÷ (4 + 2 × 8) − 8.

    $160 \div (4 + \underline{2 \times 8}) - 8$

    = $160 \div \underline{(4 + 16)} - 8$

    = 160 ÷ 20 − 8

    = 8 − 8

    =

    Calculations in parentheses are done first.

6. Find the value of $160 ÷ \{[(4 + 2) × 8] − 8\}$

$160 ÷ \{[(\underline{4 + 2}) × 8] − 8\}$

$= 160 ÷ \{[6 × 8] − 8\}$

$= 160 ÷ \{48 − 8\}$

$= 160 ÷ 40$

$=$ ▢

When you have more than one set of parentheses, brackets, or braces, do the calculations for the innermost set first.

7. Find the value of $3 + 6 × (5 + 4) ÷ 3 − 7$.

$3 + 6 × (5 + 4) ÷ 3 − 7$

$= 3 + 6 ×$  $÷ 3 − 7$

$= 3 +$ ▢ $÷ 3 − 7$

$= 3 +$ ▢ $− 7$

$=$ ▢ $− 7$

$=$ ▢

8. Find the value of $(3 + 6) × ((5 + 4) ÷ 3) − 7$.

9. Find the value of each of the following expressions.
   (a) $372 − (45 − 29)$
   (b) $372 − 45 + 29$
   (c) $372 − 45 − 29$
   (d) $372 − (45 + 29)$
   (e) $128 ÷ 4 ÷ 2$
   (f) $128 ÷ (4 × 2)$
   (g) $128 ÷ 4 × 2$
   (h) $128 ÷ (4 ÷ 2)$

10. Find the value of each of the following expressions.
   (a) $9 + 6 × (8 − 5)$
   (b) $5 × 8 + 6 ÷ 6 − 12 × 2$
   (c) $(14 − 5) ÷ (9 − 6)$
   (d) $9 − 5 ÷ (8 − 3) × 2 + 6$

11. Find the value of each of the following expressions.
    (a)  [(5 + 30) ÷ 5 + 2] ÷ 3
    (b)  16 ÷ 2 × [8 − 3 × (4 − 2)] + 1
    (c)  [(6 + 30 ÷ 6) × 5 − 5] ÷ 10 − 3

12. Which of the following is the correct interpretation of 3 times the sum of 26 and 4?
    (A)  3 × (26 + 4)        (B)  3 × 26 + 4        (C)  26 + 4 × 3

13. Write an expression for the following. Then evaluate it.

    The product of 9 and the difference between 5 and 14.

Exercise 1, pages 30–32

14. Briana has 6 scenic postcards and 4 animal postcards from each of the 8 places that she has visited. Show the number of postcards Briana has with an array.

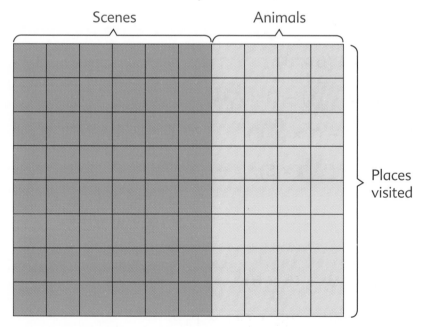

Find the total number of postcards.

**Method 1:**           **Method 2:**
(6 + 4) × 8             (6 × 8) + (4 × 8)

Do both methods give the same answer?

33

15. Is the value of (a) and (b) the same? Use a model to explain.
    - (a) $(10 - 4) \times 3$
    - (b) $(10 \times 3) - (4 \times 3)$

16. Find the missing numbers.
    - (a) $(20 + 5) \times 3 = (20 \times \boxed{\phantom{0}}) + (5 \times \boxed{\phantom{0}})$
    - (b) $(50 - 7) \times 8 = (\boxed{\phantom{0}} \times 8) - (\boxed{\phantom{0}} \times 8)$
    - (c) $7 \times (4 + 3) = (7 \times \boxed{\phantom{0}}) + (7 \times \boxed{\phantom{0}})$
    - (d) $3 \times (12 - 2) = (3 \times 12) - (3 \times \boxed{\phantom{0}})$
    - (e) $(3 \times 4) + (3 \times 5) = 3 \times (4 + \boxed{\phantom{0}})$
    - (f) $(10 \times 72) - (10 \times 28) = 10 \times (72 - \boxed{\phantom{0}})$

17. Find the missing numbers.
    - (a) $(20 + 4) \times 3 = (20 \times 3) + (\boxed{\phantom{0}} \times 3)$
    - (b) $24 \times 3 = (20 \times \boxed{\phantom{0}}) + (4 \times \boxed{\phantom{0}})$
    - (c) $36 \times 8 = (\boxed{\phantom{0}} \times 8) + (6 \times 8)$
    - (d) $(70 - 1) \times 4 = (70 \times \boxed{\phantom{0}}) - (1 \times \boxed{\phantom{0}})$
    - (e) $69 \times 4 = (70 \times \boxed{\phantom{0}}) - (1 \times \boxed{\phantom{0}})$
    - (f) $99 \times 8 = (100 \times 8) - (\boxed{\phantom{0}} \times 8)$

18. Without finding the value of each expression, copy and write
    >, <, or = in each ⬤.
    - (a) $(5 + 8) \times 6$ ⬤ $(5 \times 6) + (6 \times 6)$
    - (b) $32 \times (25 + 15)$ ⬤ $(40 \times 25) + (32 \times 15)$
    - (c) $8 \times (4 + 3)$ ⬤ $(8 \times 3) + (8 \times 4)$

Exercise 2, pages 33–34

# 2 Methods for Mental Calculation

$99

$398

$99 = $100 − $1

(a) Find the total cost of the oven and fan.

$398 + $99 = $▢    398 + 99 = 398 + 100 − 1

The total cost is $▢.

(b) How much more does the oven cost than the fan?

$398 − $99 = $▢    398 − 99 = 398 − 100 + 1

The oven costs $▢ more than the fan.

(c) How much do 3 such fans cost?

$99 × 3 = $▢    99 × 3 = 100 × 3 − 3

3 fans cost $▢.

Add.

1. (a) 299 + 42
   (c) 699 + 311
   (e) 301 + 269
   (b) 152 + 399
   (d) 39 + 201
   (f) 509 + 401

2. (a) 283 + 107
   (c) 635 + 305
   (e) 639 + 450
   (b) 314 + 206
   (d) 467 + 230
   (f) 164 + 240

Subtract.

3. (a) 307 − 99
   (c) 635 − 99
   (e) 509 − 399
   (b) 417 − 99
   (d) 433 − 299
   (f) 789 − 499

4. (a) 785 − 450
   (c) 872 − 470
   (e) 200 − 48
   (b) 654 − 330
   (d) 400 − 53
   (f) 600 − 75

5. Write an equation for each of the following word problems.
   Solve using mental math.

   (a) Angie earned $799 in the first month. In the second month,
       she earned $287 more than in the first month. How much
       did she earn in the second month?

   (b) Mr. Wilson bought a refrigerator at a sale. He paid the
       cashier $1,000 and received $199 change. How much did
       the refrigerator cost?

Exercise 3, pages 35–37

6. (a) Multiply 45 by 3.

$45 \times 3 = 40 \times 3 + 5 \times 3$
$= 120 + 15$
$=$ ▢

$4\ 5 \times 3 = 4\ 0 \times 3 + 5 \times 3$

(b) Multiply 45 by 30.

$45 \times 30 = 45 \times 3 \times 10$
$= 135 \times 10$
$=$ ▢

7. Multiply.
   (a) $74 \times 2$
   (b) $48 \times 3$
   (c) $67 \times 4$
   (d) $36 \times 7$
   (e) $94 \times 5$
   (f) $83 \times 6$
   (g) $36 \times 20$
   (h) $25 \times 40$
   (i) $76 \times 50$
   (j) $62 \times 70$
   (k) $43 \times 60$
   (l) $29 \times 80$

8. Multiply 38 by 41.

$38 \times 41 = 38 \times 40 + 38$
$= 1,520 + 38$
$=$ ▢

9. Multiply.
   (a) $45 \times 11$
   (b) $26 \times 51$
   (c) $18 \times 61$
   (d) $69 \times 31$
   (e) $71 \times 71$
   (f) $35 \times 81$

10. (a) Multiply 43 by 99.

$43 \times 99 = 43 \times 100 - 43$
$= 4,300 - 43$
$= \boxed{\phantom{00}}$

(b) Multiply 76 by 49.

$76 \times 49 = 76 \times 50 - 76$
$= 3,800 - 76$
$= \boxed{\phantom{00}}$

11. Multiply.

(a) $56 \times 99$
(b) $72 \times 99$
(c) $99 \times 84$
(d) $75 \times 59$
(e) $37 \times 39$
(f) $69 \times 56$

12. Multiply 24 by 25.

$24 \times 25 = 6 \times 4 \times 25$
$= 6 \times 100$
$= \boxed{\phantom{00}}$

4 × 25 = 100

13. Multiply.

(a) $16 \times 25$
(b) $28 \times 25$
(c) $52 \times 25$
(d) $25 \times 48$
(e) $25 \times 32$
(f) $25 \times 64$

14. Write an equation for each of the following word problems. Solve using mental math.

(a) A group of students was divided into 21 teams.
There were 28 students in each team.
How many students were there in the group?

(b) There were 36 students in a class.
Each student sold 25 tickets for a school fair.
How many tickets were sold by the class?

(c) Roger bought 6 dining chairs at $99 each.
How much did he pay for the chairs altogether?

Exercise 4, pages 38–41

# ③ Looking Back: Word Problems

Alicia bought 420 mangoes for $378. She packed the mangoes in bags of 4 mangoes each and sold all the mangoes at $6 per bag. How much money did she earn?

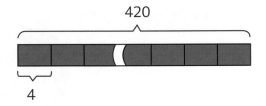

420

4

4 mangoes in 1 bag.

420 mangoes in ⬜ bags.

$420 \div 4 = 105$

There were 105 bags of mangoes.

1 bag for $6.

105 bags for $⬜.

$\$6 \times 105 = \$630$

Alicia sold the mangoes for $630.

Amount mangoes were sold for − Original cost of mangoes = ⬜

$\$630 - \$378 = \$⬜$

Alicia earned $⬜.

1.  Ryan and Juan shared $410 between them.
    Ryan received $100 more than Juan.
    How much money did Juan receive?

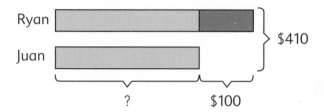

Give Ryan $100 first and divide the remaining money into two units.

2 units = $410 − $100
        = $310

1 unit = $☐

Juan received $☐.

2.  Mary bought 3 dresses. Each dress cost the same amount.
    She gave the cashier $100 and got $16 change.
    How much did each dress cost?

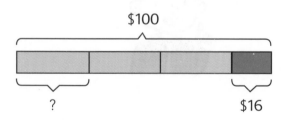

3 units = $100 − $16

       = ☐

1 unit = $☐

Each dress cost $☐.

3. Peter collected a total of 1,170 stamps.
   He collected 4 times as many US stamps as foreign stamps.
   How many US stamps did he collect?

4. Solve the following word problems using models. Compare your model and solution method to your classmates' and explain your reasoning.
   (a) John is 15 kg heavier than Peter.
       Their total mass is 127 kg.
       Find John's mass.
   (b) There are 3 times as many boys as girls.
       If there are 24 more boys than girls, how many children are there altogether?
   (c) The total mass of Peter, David, and Henry is 123 kg.
       Peter is 15 kg heavier than David.
       David is 3 kg lighter than Henry.
       Find Henry's mass.
   (d) Pablo has $180 and Ryan has $150.
       How much money must Pablo give Ryan so that they each will have an equal amount of money?
   (e) Harry bought 155 oranges for $35.
       He found that 15 of them were rotten.
       He sold all the remaining oranges at 7 for $2.
       How much money did he earn?

Exercise 5, pages 42—44

5. Mr. Given bought 2 similar T-shirts and a belt.
   He paid $50 to the cashier and received $3 change.
   If the belt cost $29, find the cost of each T-shirt.

   $50 − $3 = $47

   Mr. Given spent $47.

The total cost of 2
T-shirts and 1 belt is $47.

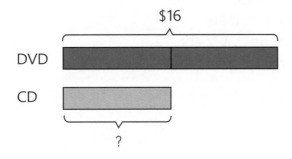

   $47 − $29 = $18

   The T-shirts cost $18.

   $18 ÷ 2 = $☐

   The cost of each T-shirt was $☐.

6. Henry bought a DVD and 3 CDs.
   The DVD cost $16.
   If a DVD cost twice as much as a CD,
   how much did he spend altogether?

$16

DVD

CD

?

   $16 ÷ 2 = $8

   A CD cost $8.

$8 \times 3 = \$24$

The cost of 3 CDs was \$24.

$\$24 + \$16 = \$\boxed{\phantom{00}}$

Henry spent $\$\boxed{\phantom{00}}$ altogether.

He bought 3 CDs and 1 DVD.

7. Solve the following word problems using models. Compare your model and solution method to your classmates' and explain your reasoning.
   (a) Matthew has twice as many stickers as David.
       How many stickers must Matthew give David
       so that they each will have 120 stickers?
   (b) Peter has twice as many stickers as Joe.
       Joe has 40 more stickers than Emily.
       They have 300 stickers altogether.
       How many stickers does Peter have?
   (c) At a book fair, Joe bought 24 books at 3 for \$5
       and had \$2 left.
       How much money did he have at first?
   (d) Ryan bought 3 similar books and a magazine.
       He paid \$30 to the cashier and received \$5 change.
       If the magazine cost twice as much as each book,
       find the cost of the magazine.
   (e) John and Paul spent \$45 altogether.
       John and Henry spent \$65 altogether.
       If Henry spent 3 times as much as Paul,
       how much did John spend?

Exercise 6, pages 45–47

# ④ Multiplication by a 2-Digit Whole Number

(a)  Multiply 78 by 30.

$78 \times 30 =$ ▢

1 unit = 78
30 units = ?

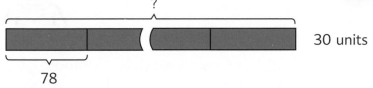

?

78

30 units

**Method 1:**

$$78 \times 3\mathbf{0} = 78 \times 3 \times \mathbf{10}$$
$$= 234 \times \mathbf{10}$$
$$= 2,34\mathbf{0}$$

Multiply 78 by 3 first.

$$\begin{array}{r} 7\,8 \\ \times \quad 3 \\ \hline 2\,3\,4 \end{array}$$

**Method 2:**

$$\begin{array}{r} 7\,8 \\ \times \quad 3\mathbf{0} \\ \hline 2,3\,4\,0 \end{array}$$

**Method 3:**

|  | 70 | 8 |  |
|---|---|---|---|
| 30 | 70 × 30 = 2,100 | 8 × 30 = 240 | |

$$\begin{array}{r} 2,1\,0\,0 \\ + \quad 2\,4\,0 \\ \hline 2,3\,4\,0 \end{array}$$

(b)  Multiply 650 by 40.

$$\begin{array}{r} 6\,5\,0 \\ \times \quad 4\mathbf{0} \\ \hline 2\,6,0\,0\,0 \end{array}$$

Multiply.

1.  (a)
    $$\begin{array}{r} 53 \\ \times\ \ 60 \\ \hline \end{array}$$

    (b)
    $$\begin{array}{r} 247 \\ \times\ \ 80 \\ \hline \end{array}$$

2.  Multiply.
    (a)  58 × 80              (b)  46 × 50
    (c)  27 × 90              (d)  207 × 60
    (e)  739 × 40             (f)  641 × 70

3.  Multiply.
    (a)
    $$\begin{array}{r} 24 \\ \times\ \ 13 \\ \hline 72 \\ 240 \\ \hline 312 \end{array}$$
    72 ← 24 × 3
    240 ← 24 × 10

    |     | 20 | 4 |
    |-----|----|----|
    | 10  | 20 × 10 = 200 | 4 × 10 = 40 |
    | 3   | 20 × 3 = 60 | 4 × 3 = 12 |

    $$\begin{array}{r} 200 \\ 40 \\ 60 \\ +\ \ 12 \\ \hline 312 \end{array}$$

    (b)
    $$\begin{array}{r} 52 \\ \times\ \ 47 \\ \hline \end{array}$$

    (c)
    $$\begin{array}{r} 325 \\ \times\ \ 54 \\ \hline 1,300 \\ 16,250 \\ \hline \end{array}$$
    1,300 ← 325 × 4
    16,250 ← 325 × 50

    |     | 300 | 20 | 5 |
    |-----|-----|----|----|
    | 50  | 300 × 50 = 15,000 | 20 × 50 = 1,000 | 5 × 50 = 250 |
    | 4   | 300 × 4 = 1,200 | 20 × 4 = 80 | 5 × 4 = 20 |

    $$\begin{array}{r} 15,000 \\ 1,000 \\ 250 \\ 1,200 \\ 80 \\ +\ \ 20 \\ \hline \end{array}$$

    (d)
    $$\begin{array}{r} 618 \\ \times\ \ 72 \\ \hline \end{array}$$

4. Multiply.

    (a) 67 × 44               (b) 53 × 48

    (c) 29 × 96               (d) 236 × 82

    (e) 457 × 35             (f) 606 × 47

5. Multiply.

    (a)
$$\begin{array}{r} 4,635 \\ \times\ \ \ \ 26 \\ \hline \end{array}$$

    (b)
$$\begin{array}{r} 8,247 \\ \times\ \ \ \ 38 \\ \hline \end{array}$$

6. Multiply.

    (a) 3,059 × 53          (b) 7,105 × 62

    (c) 2,537 × 48          (d) 3,860 × 69

    (e) 6,394 × 57          (f) 5,482 × 74

7. Solve the following word problems.

    (a) A cook uses 12 cups of water to make a pot of soup.
        How many cups of water does he need if he
        wants to make 36 pots of soup?

    (b) Mr. Kent buys a car and pays by installments.
        Each installment is $827.
        If he still has to pay $280 after paying
        72 installments, how much does the car cost?

    (c) Miss Lee sold 2,034 concert tickets at $16 per ticket.
        She also sold 840 programs at $3 each.
        How much money did she collect altogether?

    (d) In a competition, 70 students were divided equally
        into 14 teams.
        In each team there were 2 girls.
        How many boys were there altogether?

Exercise 7, pages 48—50

# 5 Division by a 2-Digit Whole Number

(a) Divide 140 by 20.

$140 \div 20 =$ ▢

1 unit = 20
? units = 140

140

? units

20

**Method 1:**
$140 \div 20 = 7$

$140 \div 20$

**Method 2:**

```
      7
20 ) 1 4 0
     1 4 0
         0
```

$7 \times 20 = 140$

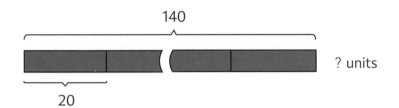

(b) Divide 150 by 20.

```
      7
20 ) 1 5 0
     1 4 0
       1 0
```

$150 \div 20$
I cannot divide 15 by 2 exactly.
So I use method 2.

1. Divide.

   (a)
   $$30 \overline{)\ 70}$$

   (b)
   $$60 \overline{)\ 430}$$

   (c)
   $$20 \overline{)\ 89}$$

   (d)
   $$70 \overline{)\ 625}$$

2. Divide.

   (a)  $90 \div 50$         (b)  $79 \div 40$         (c)  $85 \div 30$
   (d)  $540 \div 70$        (e)  $613 \div 90$        (f)  $438 \div 60$

3. Divide 74 by 21.

   $$21 \overline{)\ 74} \quad \begin{array}{r} 3 \\ \hline 63 \\ \hline 11 \end{array}$$

   The estimated quotient is 3.

   $$20 \overline{)\ 74} \quad \text{3 above}$$

   $20 \times ? = 70 \qquad 3$

   | 20 | 1 |
   |----|---|
   | 60 | 3 |
   | 63 | |

   $$\begin{array}{r} 74 \\ -63 \\ \hline 11 \end{array} \quad 11 < 21$$

   $74 \div 21 = 3 \text{ R } 11$
   $21 \times 3 + 11 = 74$

4. Divide 256 by 47.

   $$47 \overline{)\ 256} \quad \begin{array}{r} 5 \\ \hline 235 \\ \hline 21 \end{array}$$

   $$50 \overline{)\ 256} \quad \text{5 above}$$

   The estimated quotient is 5.

   $40 \times ? = 200 \qquad 5$

   | 40 | 7 |
   |----|---|
   | 200 | 35 |
   | 235 | |

   $$\begin{array}{r} 256 \\ -235 \\ \hline 21 \end{array} \quad 21 < 47$$

   $256 \div 47 = 5 \text{ R } 21$
   $47 \times 5 + 21 = 256$

5. Divide.

   (a) $63 \div 17$    (b) $48 \div 23$    (c) $85 \div 38$
   (d) $76 \div 34$    (e) $94 \div 43$    (f) $57 \div 29$
   (g) $149 \div 67$   (h) $509 \div 84$   (i) $756 \div 95$
   (j) $668 \div 72$   (k) $279 \div 56$   (l) $183 \div 44$

Exercise 8, page 51

6. Divide 89 by 24.

   $$\overset{4}{20\,)\,89}$$

   The estimated quotient is 4.

   $$\overset{4}{24\,)\,89} \quad \overset{3}{24\,)\,89}$$
   $$\phantom{24\,)\,}96 \qquad \phantom{24\,)\,}72$$
   $$\phantom{24\,)\,96}\overline{\phantom{00}} \qquad \phantom{24\,)\,}\overline{17}$$

   The estimated quotient 4
   is too big. Try 3.

   $20 \times ? = 80$

   |     | 20 | 4  |
   |-----|----|----|
   | 4̸  | 8̸0̸ | 1̸6̸ |
   | 3   | 60 | 12 |
   |     | 72 |    |

   89
   $-96$  Too big
   $-72$
   $\phantom{-}17$  $17 < 24$

   $89 \div 24 = 3 \text{ R } 17$
   $24 \times 3 + 17 = 89$

7. Divide 78 by 26.

   $$\overset{2}{30\,)\,78}$$

   The estimated quotient is 2.

   $$\overset{2}{26\,)\,78} \quad \overset{3}{26\,)\,78}$$
   $$\phantom{26\,)\,}52 \qquad \phantom{26\,)\,}78$$
   $$\phantom{26\,)\,}\overline{26} \qquad \phantom{26\,)\,}\overline{\phantom{0}0}$$

   The estimated quotient 2
   is too small. Try 3.

   $20 \times ? = 70$

   |      | 20 | 6  |
   |------|----|----|
   | 2    | 40 | 12 |
   | $+1$ | 20 | 6  |
   | 3    | 78 |    |

   78
   $-52$
   $\phantom{-}26$
   $-26$
   $\phantom{-0}0$

   $78 \div 26 = 3$
   $26 \times 3 = 78$

49

8. Divide.
   (a) $68 \div 17$     (b) $77 \div 25$     (c) $94 \div 33$
   (d) $83 \div 21$     (e) $84 \div 43$     (f) $75 \div 15$

9. Divide 285 by 33.

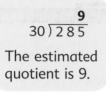

The estimated quotient is 9.

$$\begin{array}{r} 9 \\ 30\overline{)285} \end{array}$$

$$\begin{array}{r} 9 \\ 33\overline{)285} \\ 297 \end{array} \quad \Rightarrow \quad \begin{array}{r} 8 \\ 33\overline{)285} \\ 264 \\ \hline 21 \end{array}$$

The estimated quotient 9 is too big. Try 8.

$30 \times ? = 200$

$30 \times ? = 80$

| | | 30 | 3 |
|---|---|---|---|
| 6 | | 180 | 18 |
| +2 | | 60 | 6 |
| 8 | | | 264 |

$$\begin{array}{r} 285 \\ -198 \\ \hline 87 \\ -66 \\ \hline 21 \end{array}$$

$285 \div 33 = 8 \text{ R } 21$
$33 \times 8 + 21 = 285$

10. Divide 473 by 78.

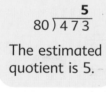

The estimated quotient is 5.

$$\begin{array}{r} 5 \\ 80\overline{)473} \end{array}$$

$$\begin{array}{r} 5 \\ 78\overline{)473} \\ 390 \\ \hline 83 \end{array} \quad \Rightarrow \quad \begin{array}{r} 6 \\ 78\overline{)473} \\ 468 \\ \hline 5 \end{array}$$

The estimated quotient 5 is too small. Try 6.

$70 \times ? = 400$

$70 \times ? = 80$

| | | 70 | 8 |
|---|---|---|---|
| 5 | | 350 | 40 |
| +1 | | 70 | 8 |
| 6 | | | 468 |

$$\begin{array}{r} 473 \\ -390 \\ \hline 83 \\ -78 \\ \hline 5 \end{array}$$

$473 \div 78 = 6 \text{ R } 5$
$78 \times 6 + 5 = 473$

11. Divide.
    (a) $207 \div 23$
    (b) $236 \div 39$
    (c) $474 \div 79$
    (d) $572 \div 64$
    (e) $464 \div 58$
    (f) $640 \div 93$

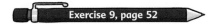
Exercise 9, page 52

12. Divide 570 by 16.

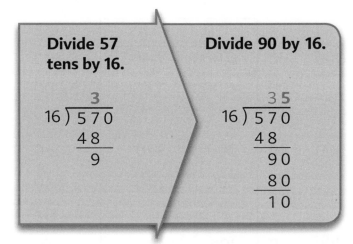

**Divide 57 tens by 16.**

$$
\begin{array}{r}
3\phantom{00} \\
16 \overline{)\ 5\ 7\ 0} \\
4\ 8\phantom{0} \\
\hline
9\phantom{0}
\end{array}
$$

**Divide 90 by 16.**

$$
\begin{array}{r}
3\,5\phantom{0} \\
16 \overline{)\ 5\ 7\ 0} \\
4\ 8\phantom{0} \\
\hline
9\ 0 \\
8\ 0 \\
\hline
1\ 0
\end{array}
$$

| | 10 | 6 | 570 | |
|---|---|---|---|---|
| $10 \times ? = 500$ | ~~50~~ | ~~500~~ | ~~300~~ | ~~−800~~ Too big |
| | ~~40~~ | ~~400~~ | ~~240~~ | ~~−640~~ Too big |
| | 30 | 300 | 180 | −480 |
| | | | | 90 |
| $10 \times ? = 90$ | ~~9~~ | ~~90~~ | ~~54~~ | ~~−144~~ Too big |
| | ~~7~~ | ~~70~~ | ~~42~~ | ~~−112~~ Too big |
| | +5 | 50 | 30 | −80 |
| | 35 | 560 | | 10 |

$570 \div 16 = 35$ R $10$
$16 \times 35 + 10 = 570$

13. Divide.

(a)
$$
\begin{array}{r}
2\ 5 \\
34 \overline{)\ 8\ 7\ 0} \\
6\ 8\phantom{0} \\
\hline
1\ 9\ 0 \\
1\ 7\ 0 \\
\hline
2\ 0
\end{array}
$$

(b)
$$
\begin{array}{r}
3\ 0 \\
28 \overline{)\ 8\ 6\ 2} \\
8\ 4\phantom{0} \\
\hline
2\ 2
\end{array}
$$

(c)
$$
47 \overline{)\ 7\ 0\ 3}
$$

(d)
$$
15 \overline{)\ 6\ 1\ 2}
$$

14. Divide.

    (a)  552 ÷ 24                (b)  660 ÷ 29

    (c)  925 ÷ 46                (d)  399 ÷ 31

    (e)  708 ÷ 67                (f)  374 ÷ 18

Exercise 10, page 53

15. Divide.

(a)

$$
\begin{array}{r}
234 \\
28\,\overline{)\,6{,}552} \\
5\,6\phantom{00} \\
\hline
9\,5\phantom{0} \\
8\,4\phantom{0} \\
\hline
1\,1\,2 \\
1\,1\,2 \\
\hline
0
\end{array}
$$

$20 \times ? = 6{,}000$

$20 \times ? = \phantom{0}900$

$20 \times ? = \phantom{0}100$

| | 20 | 8 | 6,552 |
|---|---|---|---|
| ~~300~~ | ~~6,000~~ | ~~2,400~~ | −~~8,400~~  Too bi |
| 200 | 4,000 | 1,600 | −5,600 |
| | | | 952 |
| ~~40~~ | ~~800~~ | ~~320~~ | −~~1,120~~  Too bi |
| 30 | 600 | 240 | −840 |
| | | | 112 |
| ~~5~~ | ~~100~~ | ~~40~~ | −~~140~~  Too bi |
| +4 | 80 | 32 | −112 |
| 234 | 6,552 | | 0 |

$6{,}552 \div 28 = 234$

$28 \times 234 = 6{,}552$

(b)

$$
\begin{array}{r}
83 \\
52\,\overline{)\,4{,}328} \\
4\,1\,6\phantom{0} \\
\hline
1\,6\,8 \\
1\,5\,6 \\
\hline
1\,2
\end{array}
$$

(c)

$$
64\,\overline{)\,6{,}820}
$$

(d)

$$
45\,\overline{)\,3{,}185}
$$

16. Divide.
    (a)  6,692 ÷ 28
    (b)  2,409 ÷ 18
    (c)  1,495 ÷ 45
    (d)  6,008 ÷ 56
    (e)  1,054 ÷ 37
    (f)  9,864 ÷ 29

17. Solve the following word problems.
    (a)  Mr. Hill has to drive to a city which is 240 km from Portland.
         If his car can travel 15 km on 1 L of gas, how many liters
         of gas does he need for the trip?
    (b)  In a fair, 1,064 balloons were shared equally among 38 students.
         How many balloons did each student receive?
    (c)  Mrs. Garcia sold 96 figurines at a garage sale.
         The figurines were sold in boxes of 12.
         She sold all the figurines at $7 per box.
         How much money did she receive?
    (d)  Mrs. Ward bought 840 eggs.
         She sold them in trays of 12 eggs each.
         How much money did she receive if the
         selling price per tray was $3?

Exercise 11, pages 54—55

1. Which expression will give the answer to the following problem?
   Sarah packed 128 cookies equally into 8 boxes. She gave
   3 boxes away. How many cookies does she have left?
   (A) $128 - 3 \times (128 \div 8)$         (B) $5 \times (128 \div 8)$
   (C) $128 - 128 \div 8 \times 3$           (D) $128 - 128 \div (8 \times 3)$

2. _____ $\div 7 = 35$ R 3. What is the number in the blank?
   (A) 5        (B) 105        (C) 245        (D) 248

3. Alex has 76 cards. Gene has 24 fewer cards than Alex.
   How many cards must Alex give to Gene so they both have
   the same number?
   (A) 12        (B) 24        (C) 26        (D) 50

4. Select True or False.
   (a) $20 - 8 \div 2 \times 4 + 1 = 25$           True / False
   (b) $95 \times 8 = (100 \times 8) - (5 \times 8)$      True / False

5. Select True or False.
   (a) 600 stickers are put in packets of 24.
       There are 25 packets.                  True / False
   (b) Tank 1 has 34 fish and Tank 2 has 20 fish.
       If 7 fish are moved from Tank 1 to Tank 2,
       both tanks will have the same number of fish.    True / False

6. Find the value of each of the following expressions.
   (a) $12 \div (6 - 2) + 7 \times 2$            (b) $24 - 8 \div 2 \times 5 + 1$
   (c) $6 \times (5 + 6) - 18 + 8$         (d) $(7 - 3) \times 3 + 9 \div 3$
   (e) $2 \times (28 + 36) - 49$           (f) $78 + 21 \div 3 - (6 + 25)$
   (g) $50 - (225 \div 15 + 13)$         (h) $29 + (300 \div 10 - 3 \times 9)$
   (i) $60 \div (14 - 4) \times 3$             (j) $50 - 8 \times 2 + 16 \div 8$
   (k) $[64 - (24 - 18)] \times 10$        (l) $15 \div 3 + ((9 - 6) \times 4)$
   (m) $5 + 2 \times \{[3 + (2 \times 4 - 1) + 3] - 7\}$
   (n) $((8 \times (2 + 1)) - 6) \div 9$

7. Find the value of each of the following expressions.
   (a) $28 + 19 - 24$
   (b) $12 - 9 \times 5 \div 15$
   (c) $(42 + 14) \div 7 \times 5$
   (d) $(59 + 13) \div (4 \times 2)$
   (e) $12 - 4 \div 2 + 6$
   (f) $24 + 6 \times 7 \div 3$
   (g) $(4 + 8) \times 3 \div 4$
   (h) $25 - (7 + 9 \times 2) \div 5$
   (i) $23 \times (34 - 25)$
   (j) $7 \times 8 + 48 \div 3$
   (k) $(45 - 31) \times 4 + 12$
   (l) $(28 + 9) \times (12 - 7)$
   (m) $16 + 3 \times 8 \div 4$
   (n) $30 + 85 \times 2 \div (8 + 9)$
   (o) $(220 \div 11) \times (28 - 5)$
   (p) $[12 + (30 - 14)] \div 4 \times 5$

8. What is the greatest whole number that will make each statement true?
   (a) $75 + \boxed{\phantom{x}} < 100$
   (b) $\boxed{\phantom{x}} - 97 < 10^2$
   (c) $36 \times \boxed{\phantom{x}} < 150$
   (d) $95 - \boxed{\phantom{x}} > 18$

9. What is the missing number in each $\boxed{\phantom{x}}$?
   (a) $(29 \times 4) = (25 \times 4) + (\boxed{\phantom{x}} \times 4)$
   (b) $(29 \times 4) = (30 \times 4) - (\boxed{\phantom{x}} \times 4)$
   (c) $64 - (24 - 18) \times 10 = 64 - \boxed{\phantom{x}}$
   (d) $3 \times 159 = (3 \times 160) - (3 \times \boxed{\phantom{x}})$
   (e) $36 \times 25 = 9 \times \boxed{\phantom{x}}$
   (f) $7 \times 45 = 21 \times \boxed{\phantom{x}}$
   (g) $25 \times 24 = 100 \times \boxed{\phantom{x}}$
   (h) $15 \times 18 = 3 \times \boxed{\phantom{x}}$
   (i) $8 + 8 + 6 \times 2 = \boxed{\phantom{x}} \times 6 + 28$
   (j) $46 \times 7 = (40 \times \boxed{\phantom{x}}) + (6 \times \boxed{\phantom{x}})$

10. Multiply.
    (a)  62 × 99          (b)  84 × 29          (c)  76 × 25

11. Add or subtract.
    (a)  698 + 83         (b)  943 − 499        (c)  1,248 + 399

12. Multiply.
    (a)  71 × 29          (b)  86 × 36          (c)  35 × 94
    (d)  258 × 24         (e)  574 × 62         (f)  392 × 44
    (g)  7,067 × 39       (h)  6,830 × 72       (i)  4,872 × 44

13. Multiply or divide.
    (a)  2650 × 600       (b)  34,400 × 80      (c)  1,290 ÷ 80
    (d)  52 × 75          (e)  994 ÷ 71         (f)  301 ÷ 24

14. What is the missing number in each 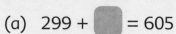 ?

    (a)  299 + ⬛ = 605

    (b)  350 − ⬛ = 186

    (c)  8 × ⬛ = 736

    (d)  98 ÷ ⬛ = 7

15. Multiply or divide.
    (a)  36 × 28          (b)  615 × 32         (c)  864 ÷ 36

16. Divide.
    (a)  76 ÷ 23          (b)  95 ÷ 64          (c)  81 ÷ 38
    (d)  510 ÷ 67         (e)  337 ÷ 72         (f)  409 ÷ 53
    (g)  3,640 ÷ 57       (h)  5,509 ÷ 63       (i)  8,513 ÷ 36

17. A number when divided by 32 has a quotient of 8 with 3
    as the remainder. Find the number.

18. Peter put 1,827 books equally on 43 shelves.
    (a)  How many books were there on each shelf?
    (b)  How many books were left over?

19. There are 2,204 children in a school.
    Of them, 925 are girls.
    How many more boys than girls are there?

20. 3 pieces of ribbon, each 85 cm long, are cut from a length of ribbon
    3 m long. What is the length of the remaining piece of ribbon?

21. Peter, John, and Dan shared $1,458 equally.
    Peter used part of his share to buy a bicycle and had $139 left.
    What was the cost of the bicycle?

22. Oranges are packed in a box in 4 layers.
    Each layer has 6 rows of oranges with 8 oranges in each row.
    How many oranges are there in the box?

23. David is 18 lb lighter than Pablo.
    Their total weight is 250 lb.
    Find David's weight.

24. Brett picked 257 cherries from one tree and 493 from another.
    He sold all the cherries at 50 for $3.
    How much money did he receive?

25. Aaron saved twice as much as Roger.
    Maria saved $60 more than Roger. If they saved $600 altogether,
    how much did Maria save?

26. Paul picked 357 lemons the first day and 497 lemons the next day.
    He packed the lemons in bags of 12.
    (a)  How many lemons did he have left over?
    (b)  If he sold each bag of lemons for $2, how much money did
         he receive?

27. Mr. Dunlap bought 40 boxes of grapefruit for $258.
    There were 24 grapefruit in each box.
    He threw away 15 rotten grapefruit and sold the rest at 3 for $1.
    How much money did he earn?

28. Lily has $25.
Mary has $10 more than Lily.
Amber has 3 times as much money as Mary.
How much money do the 3 girls have altogether?

29. A man had 15 crates of limes.
Each crate had the same number of limes.
He sold 70 limes on Monday and twice as many limes on Tuesday.
He had 90 limes left.
How many limes were there in each crate at first?

30. A bakery sold 328 cakes on Monday.
It sold 178 more cakes on Monday than on Tuesday.
Each cake was sold for $19.
How much money did the bakery receive from selling the cakes?

31. Examine the first three equations.
Determine if they are true.
Explain any pattern you see.
Continue the pattern for the remaining expressions.

$9 \times 11 = 10 \times 10 - 1$

$8 \times 12 = 10 \times 10 - 4$

$7 \times 13 = 10 \times 10 - 9$

$6 \times 14 =$ 

$5 \times 15 =$ 

$4 \times 16 =$ 

$3 \times 17 =$ 

$2 \times 18 =$ 

$1 \times 19 =$ 

Review 2, pages 56—61

# 3 FRACTIONS

## 1 Looking Back

Which is greater, $\frac{2}{5}$ or $\frac{3}{8}$?

Use fraction discs to compare the fractions.

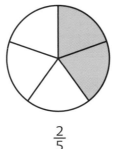

$\frac{2}{5}$

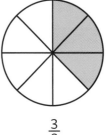

$\frac{3}{8}$

In the fraction $\frac{2}{5}$, 2 is the **numerator** and 5 is the **denominator**.

$\frac{2}{5}$

$\frac{3}{8}$

Draw fraction bars to compare the fractions.

Mark each fraction on a number line and then compare the fractions.

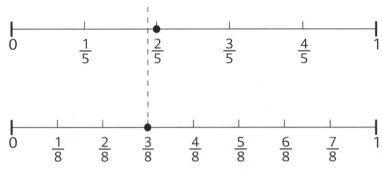

Change the fractions to **like fractions** and then compare the fractions.

$\dfrac{2}{5} \longrightarrow \dfrac{16}{40}$

$\dfrac{3}{8} \longrightarrow \dfrac{15}{40}$

**Like fractions** are fractions with common denominators. It is easy to compare like fractions. Why?

Which is smaller, $\dfrac{4}{5}$ or $\dfrac{4}{9}$?

$\dfrac{4}{9} < \dfrac{4}{5}$

Notice that the numerators are the same. $\dfrac{1}{9}$ is smaller than $\dfrac{1}{5}$ because the part is smaller. So $\dfrac{4}{9}$ must be smaller than $\dfrac{4}{5}$.

1. Copy and write **<**, **>**, or **=** for each .

(a) $\dfrac{2}{3}$  $\dfrac{3}{5}$ (b) $\dfrac{3}{5}$  $\dfrac{3}{7}$ (c) $\dfrac{4}{5}$  $\dfrac{5}{6}$

60

2. There are 12 flowers. 8 of them are roses.
   What fraction of the flowers are roses?

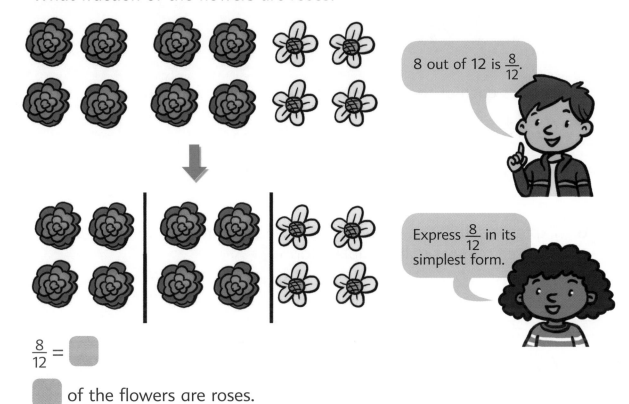

8 out of 12 is $\frac{8}{12}$.

Express $\frac{8}{12}$ in its simplest form.

$\frac{8}{12} = \boxed{\phantom{00}}$

$\boxed{\phantom{00}}$ of the flowers are roses.

3. What number does each letter represent?

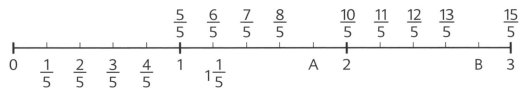

$1 + \frac{1}{5} = 1\frac{1}{5}$.

$1\frac{1}{5}$ is a **mixed number**.

A **mixed number** is made up of a whole number and a fraction.

$\frac{5}{5}$ and $\frac{6}{5}$ are improper fractions.

An **improper fraction** has a value equal to, or greater than one. The numerator is equal to, or greater than the denominator.

4. Express $\frac{11}{4}$ as a mixed number.

$$\frac{11}{4} = \frac{8}{4} + \frac{3}{4} = 2\frac{3}{4}$$

5. Express each of the following as an improper fraction.

    (a) $1\frac{4}{5}$  (b) $2\frac{2}{3}$

    (c) $2\frac{1}{4}$  (d) $2\frac{5}{6}$

6. Express each of the following as a whole number, a fraction, or a mixed number in its simplest form.

    (a) $\frac{8}{12}$  (b) $\frac{9}{12}$

    (c) $\frac{6}{9}$  (d) $\frac{6}{12}$

    (e) $\frac{13}{5}$  (f) $\frac{21}{3}$

    (g) $\frac{24}{9}$  (h) $\frac{50}{6}$

7. Copy and write >, <, or = for each .

    (a) $\frac{3}{2}$ ⬤ $\frac{5}{4}$  (b) $2\frac{1}{2}$ ⬤ $2\frac{1}{7}$

    (c) $3\frac{8}{9}$ ⬤ $4$  (d) $1\frac{5}{6}$ ⬤ $\frac{11}{6}$

    (e) $4\frac{2}{3}$ ⬤ $\frac{9}{2}$  (f) $3$ ⬤ $\frac{15}{4}$

Exercise 1, pages 62–65

# ② Fractions and Division

4 children share 3 pancakes equally.
Each child receives 3 quarters.

$$3 \div 4 = \frac{3}{4}$$

4 children share 5 pancakes equally.
Each child receives 5 quarters.

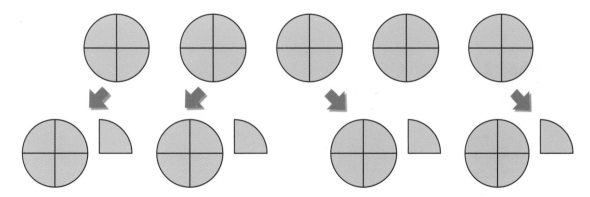

$$5 \div 4 = \frac{5}{4}$$

Here is another way to show that $5 \div 4 = \frac{5}{4}$.

$$4 \overline{)\ 5} \\ \quad \underline{4} \\ \quad 1$$

Each child receives 1 pancake first.
Share the remaining pancake.
$$1 \div 4 = \frac{1}{4}$$
Each child receives 1 and $\frac{1}{4}$ pancakes.

$5 \div 4 = 1\frac{1}{4}$

$\quad = \frac{4}{4} + \frac{1}{4}$

$\quad = \frac{5}{4}$

1. Express $\frac{11}{4}$ as a mixed number.

$\frac{11}{4} = 11 \div 4 = \boxed{\phantom{0}}$

$$4 \overline{)\ 1\ 1} \quad ^{2} \\ \quad \underline{8} \\ \quad 3$$

2. Find the value of $22 \div 8$.

**Method 1**:

$22 \div 8 = 2\frac{6}{8}$

$\qquad = 2\frac{\boxed{\phantom{0}}}{4}$

$$8 \overline{)\ 2\ 2} \quad ^{2} \\ \quad \underline{1\ 6} \\ \quad 6$$

**Method 2**:

$22 \div 8 = \frac{22}{8}$

$\qquad = \frac{\boxed{\phantom{0}}}{4}$

$\qquad = \boxed{\phantom{0}}$

3. Find the value of each of the following.
   (a)  7 ÷ 3                          (b)  14 ÷ 5
   (c)  21 ÷ 6                         (d)  77 ÷ 9

4. Mary baked 10 cakes of the same size.
   She divided the cakes into 4 equal shares.
   How many cakes were there in each share?

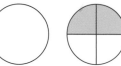

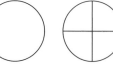

$10 ÷ 4 = \dfrac{10}{4}$

$\phantom{10 ÷ 4} = \boxed{\phantom{0}}$

There were  cakes in each share.

5. Mrs. York bought 3 m of cloth.
   She used the cloth to make 9 pillow cases of the same size.
   How much cloth in meters did she use for each pillow case?

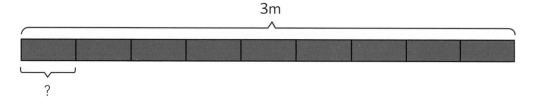

$3 ÷ 9 = \dfrac{3}{9}$

$\phantom{3 ÷ 9} = \boxed{\phantom{0}}$

Mrs. York used  m of cloth for each pillow case.

6. A red ribbon 11 m long is 5 times as long as a blue ribbon. How long is the blue ribbon?

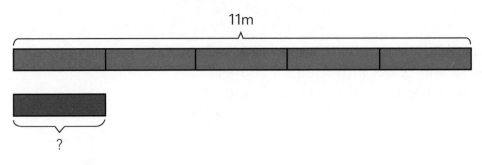

11m

?

$11 \div 5 =$ ◻

The blue ribbon is ◻ m long.

7. A bucket contains 8 qt of water. If the water is poured equally into 3 jugs, how much water is there in each jug?

$8 \div 3 =$ ◻

$$\begin{array}{r} 2 \\ 3\overline{)\,8} \\ 6 \\ \hline 2 \end{array}$$

There are ◻ qt of water in each jug.

8. A packet of flour with a mass of 4 kg was divided into 6 equal shares. What was the mass of each share in kilograms?

Exercise 2, pages 66–68

## 3 Addition and Subtraction of Unlike Fractions

Ann ate $\frac{1}{3}$ of a cake.

Her brother ate $\frac{1}{2}$ of the same cake.

What fraction of the cake did they eat altogether?

$$\frac{1}{3} + \frac{1}{2} = \frac{2}{6} + \frac{3}{6}$$

$$=$$

The cake is divided into 6 equal parts.
Ann ate 2 parts and her brother ate 3 parts.

They ate ⬜ of the cake altogether.

$\frac{1}{3}$ and $\frac{1}{2}$ do not have the same denominator.

They are called **unlike fractions.**

$\frac{2}{6}$ and $\frac{3}{6}$ have the same denominator.

They are called **like fractions.**

We can change unlike fractions to like fractions using equivalent fractions:

$\frac{1}{3}, \frac{2}{6}, ...$

$\frac{1}{2}, \frac{3}{6}, ...$

1. (a) Add $\frac{1}{3}$ and $\frac{2}{5}$.

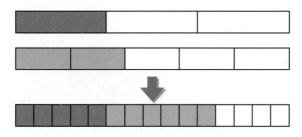

$$\frac{1}{3} + \frac{2}{5} = \frac{\square}{15} + \frac{\square}{15}$$

$$= \frac{\square}{15}$$

15 is a common multiple of 3 and 5.

(b) Add $\frac{1}{3}$ and $\frac{4}{5}$.

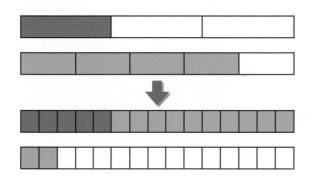

$$\frac{1}{3} + \frac{4}{5} = \frac{\square}{15} + \frac{\square}{15}$$

$$= \frac{\square}{15}$$

$$= \square$$

$\frac{1}{3}$ is less than $\frac{1}{2}$. $\frac{4}{5}$ is close to 1. We can estimate that the answer may be greater than 1 but less than $1\frac{1}{2}$.

2. Add $\frac{3}{8}$ and $\frac{1}{6}$. Will the answer be greater than 1?

Both fractions are less than $\frac{1}{2}$, so the answer will not be greater than 1.

$\frac{3}{8} + \frac{1}{6} = \frac{\Box}{24} + \frac{\Box}{24}$

$\qquad = \frac{\Box}{24}$

$\frac{3}{8}, \frac{\Box}{16}, \frac{\Box}{24}, \ldots$

$\frac{1}{6}, \ldots$

24 is a multiple of 8.
It is also a multiple of 6.

$\frac{3}{8} + \frac{1}{6} = \frac{\Box}{48} + \frac{\Box}{48}$

$\qquad = \frac{\Box}{48}$

$\qquad = \frac{\Box}{24}$

Multiply the denominators.
$8 \times 6 = 48$
48 is a multiple of both 8 and 6.

3. Add $\frac{7}{10}$ and $\frac{5}{6}$. Will the answer be greater than 1?

Both fractions are greater than $\frac{1}{2}$, so the answer will be greater than 1.

$\frac{7}{10} + \frac{5}{6} = \frac{\Box}{60} + \frac{\Box}{60}$

$\qquad = \frac{\Box}{60}$

$\qquad = \frac{\Box}{15}$

$\qquad = \Box$

$10 \times 6 = 60$.
60 is a common multiple of 10 and 6.

$\frac{7}{10} + \frac{5}{6} = \frac{\Box}{30} + \frac{\Box}{30}$

$\qquad = \frac{\Box}{30}$

$\qquad = \frac{\Box}{15}$

$\qquad = \Box$

Use the least common multiple of 10 and 6, which is 30.

4. Add. Give each answer in its simplest form.

(a) $\frac{7}{9} + \frac{5}{6}$

(b) $\frac{3}{4} + \frac{5}{12}$

(c) $\frac{3}{10} + \frac{5}{6}$

(d) $\frac{2}{3} + \frac{2}{5}$

(e) $\frac{7}{24} + \frac{5}{6}$

(f) $\frac{7}{10} + \frac{93}{100}$

Exercise 3, pages 69–70

5. Cary read $\frac{3}{4}$ of a book yesterday.

He read $\frac{2}{3}$ of it today.

What fraction more did he read yesterday than today?

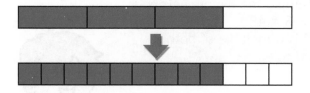

$\frac{3}{4} - \frac{2}{3} = \frac{\boxed{\phantom{0}}}{12} - \frac{\boxed{\phantom{0}}}{12}$

$= \frac{\boxed{\phantom{0}}}{12}$

12 is a common multiple of 4 and 3.

He read $\boxed{\phantom{0}}$ more yesterday than today.

6. Subtract $\frac{1}{6}$ from $\frac{7}{8}$.

$\frac{7}{8} - \frac{1}{6} = \frac{\boxed{\phantom{0}}}{24} - \frac{\boxed{\phantom{0}}}{24}$

$= \frac{\boxed{\phantom{0}}}{24}$

$\frac{7}{8}, \frac{\boxed{\phantom{0}}}{16}, \frac{\boxed{\phantom{0}}}{24}, ...$

$\frac{1}{6}, ...$

24 is a common multiple of 8 and 6.

7. Subtract $\frac{1}{10}$ from $\frac{5}{6}$.

$\frac{5}{6} - \frac{1}{10} = \frac{\boxed{\phantom{0}}}{60} - \frac{\boxed{\phantom{0}}}{60}$

$= \frac{\boxed{\phantom{0}}}{60}$

$= \frac{\boxed{\phantom{0}}}{15}$

$10 \times 6 = 60$.
I will use 60.

8. Subtract $\frac{5}{6}$ from $1\frac{7}{10}$.

Will the answer be smaller than 1?

$1\frac{7}{10} - \frac{5}{6} = 1\frac{\square}{30} - \frac{\square}{30}$

$= \frac{\square}{30} - \frac{\square}{30}$

$= \frac{\square}{30}$

$= \frac{\square}{15}$

$\frac{7}{10}, \frac{\square}{20}, \frac{\square}{30}, \ldots$

$\frac{5}{6}, \ldots$

30 is a common multiple of 10 and 6.

9. Estimate whether the answer will be smaller than 1. Then subtract.

(a) $1\frac{5}{6} - \frac{1}{2}$

$= 1\frac{5}{6} - \frac{\square}{6}$

$= 1\frac{\square}{6}$

$= \square$

(b) $1\frac{1}{6} - \frac{3}{10}$

$= 1\frac{5}{30} - \frac{9}{30}$

$= \frac{\square}{30} - \frac{9}{30}$

$= \frac{\square}{30}$

$= \square$

10. Subtract. Give each answer in its simplest form.

(a) $\frac{1}{2} - \frac{2}{5}$

(b) $\frac{2}{3} - \frac{3}{8}$

(c) $\frac{1}{4} - \frac{1}{6}$

(d) $\frac{1}{6} - \frac{1}{10}$

(e) $\frac{5}{6} - \frac{3}{10}$

(f) $\frac{9}{10} - \frac{5}{6}$

11. Subtract. Give each answer in its simplest form.

(a) $1\frac{1}{2} - \frac{3}{5}$

(b) $1\frac{2}{3} - \frac{3}{4}$

(c) $1\frac{1}{8} - \frac{5}{12}$

(d) $1\frac{1}{6} - \frac{7}{10}$

(e) $1\frac{5}{6} - \frac{9}{10}$

(f) $1\frac{3}{8} - \frac{7}{10}$

Exercise 4, pages 71–72

# 4 Addition and Subtraction of Mixed Numbers

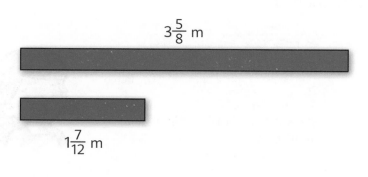

$3\frac{5}{8}$ m

$1\frac{7}{12}$ m

(a) Find the total length of $3\frac{5}{8}$ m and $1\frac{7}{12}$ m.

$$3\frac{5}{8} + 1\frac{7}{12} = 4\frac{5}{8} + \frac{7}{12}$$

$$= 4\frac{15}{24} + \frac{14}{24}$$

$$= 4\frac{\boxed{\phantom{0}}}{24}$$

$$= \boxed{\phantom{0}}$$

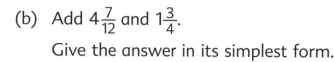

The total length is ⬜ m.

(b) Add $4\frac{7}{12}$ and $1\frac{3}{4}$.

Give the answer in its simplest form.

$$4\frac{7}{12} + 1\frac{3}{4} = 5\frac{7}{12} + \frac{3}{4}$$

$$= 5\frac{7}{12} + \frac{9}{12}$$

$$= 5\frac{\boxed{\phantom{0}}}{12}$$

$$= 5\frac{\boxed{\phantom{0}}}{3}$$

$$= \boxed{\phantom{0}}$$

$\frac{7}{12}$ and $\frac{3}{4}$ are both greater than $\frac{1}{2}$. I know the answer will be between 6 and 7.

72

1. Estimate. Then find the sum.
   All answers should be in simplest form.

   (a) $3\frac{2}{9} + 2\frac{4}{15} = 5\frac{2}{9} + \frac{4}{15}$

   $$= 5\frac{\boxed{\phantom{0}}}{135} + \frac{\boxed{\phantom{0}}}{135}$$

   $$= 5\frac{\boxed{\phantom{0}}}{135}$$

   $$= \boxed{\phantom{0}}$$

   (b) $1\frac{7}{9} + 4\frac{8}{15} = 5\frac{7}{9} + \frac{8}{15}$

   $$= 5\frac{\boxed{\phantom{0}}}{45} + \frac{\boxed{\phantom{0}}}{45}$$

   $$= 5\frac{\boxed{\phantom{0}}}{45}$$

   $$= \boxed{\phantom{0}}$$

2. Add.

   (a) $2\frac{7}{12} + 1\frac{3}{4}$          (b) $1\frac{9}{10} + 1\frac{5}{6}$          (c) $1\frac{1}{6} + 1\frac{7}{10}$

   (d) $1\frac{3}{4} + 1\frac{1}{6}$          (e) $2\frac{3}{5} + 1\frac{9}{10}$          (f) $1\frac{5}{6} + 2\frac{7}{8}$

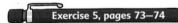

Exercise 5, pages 73–74

3. Find the difference in length between $4\frac{3}{4}$ m and $3\frac{7}{12}$ m.

   $4\frac{3}{4} - 3\frac{7}{12} = 1\frac{3}{4} - \frac{7}{12}$

   $$= 1\frac{9}{12} - \frac{7}{12}$$

   $$= 1\frac{\boxed{\phantom{0}}}{12}$$

   $$= \boxed{\phantom{0}}$$

   4 − 3 = 1.
   The answer will be around 1.

   The difference in length is  m.

4. Subtract.

(a) $3\frac{1}{6} - 1\frac{5}{9} = 2\frac{1}{6} - \frac{5}{9}$

$= 2\frac{3}{18} - \frac{10}{18}$

$= 1\frac{\boxed{\phantom{0}}}{18} - \frac{10}{18}$

$= \boxed{\phantom{0}}$

(b) $4\frac{1}{6} - 1\frac{3}{10} = 3\frac{1}{6} - \frac{3}{10}$

$= 3\frac{\boxed{\phantom{0}}}{30} - \frac{9}{30}$

$= 2\frac{\boxed{\phantom{0}}}{30} - \frac{9}{30}$

$= 2\frac{\boxed{\phantom{0}}}{30}$

$= \boxed{\phantom{0}}$

5. Estimate. Then find the difference.

(a) $3\frac{2}{5} - 1\frac{9}{10}$

$= 2\frac{2}{5} - \frac{9}{10}$

$= 2\frac{4}{10} - \frac{9}{10}$

$= 1\frac{\boxed{\phantom{0}}}{10} - \frac{9}{10}$

$= 1\frac{\boxed{\phantom{0}}}{10}$

$= \boxed{\phantom{0}}$

(b) $5\frac{1}{10} - 2\frac{5}{6}$

$= 3\frac{1}{10} - \frac{5}{6}$

$= 3\frac{3}{30} - \frac{25}{30}$

$= 2\frac{\boxed{\phantom{0}}}{30} - \frac{25}{30}$

$= 2\frac{\boxed{\phantom{0}}}{30}$

$= \boxed{\phantom{0}}$

6. Subtract.

(a) $4\frac{1}{6} - 1\frac{5}{6}$

(b) $5\frac{1}{4} - 2\frac{7}{12}$

(c) $2\frac{1}{5} - \frac{3}{4}$

(d) $4\frac{3}{8} - 2\frac{7}{10}$

(e) $3\frac{5}{6} - 2\frac{3}{4}$

(f) $3\frac{3}{10} - 1\frac{5}{6}$

Exercise 6, pages 75–76

7. Add or subtract. Give each answer in its simplest form.

(a) $\frac{7}{12} + \frac{5}{6}$

(b) $\frac{9}{10} + \frac{1}{6}$

(c) $\frac{5}{6} + \frac{7}{8}$

(d) $\frac{2}{3} - \frac{5}{12}$

(e) $\frac{5}{6} - \frac{7}{10}$

(f) $\frac{3}{4} - \frac{1}{6}$

(g) $2\frac{2}{3} + 1\frac{5}{9}$

(h) $2\frac{1}{8} + 1\frac{5}{6}$

(i) $1\frac{1}{4} + 2\frac{5}{6}$

(j) $3\frac{5}{6} - 1\frac{1}{3}$

(k) $3\frac{4}{5} - 1\frac{3}{10}$

(l) $4\frac{5}{6} - 1\frac{1}{4}$

8. Samy took $\frac{3}{4}$ hour to travel from home to the zoo.

He took $1\frac{1}{4}$ hours to return home.

How much longer did he take to return home than to go to the zoo?

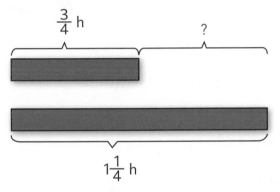

Will the answer be less than 1?

$1\frac{1}{4} - \frac{3}{4} = $ ▢

It took Samy ▢ hour longer to return home.

9. Ali went to a bookshop. He spent $\frac{3}{5}$ of his money on books and $\frac{1}{4}$ of it on a pen. What fraction of his money did he have left?

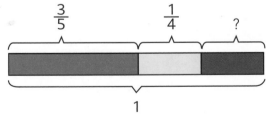

Since the whole of his money is 1, the answer must be less than 1. Will it be less than $\frac{1}{2}$?

$1 - (\frac{3}{5} + \frac{1}{4}) = $ ▢

Ali had ▢ of his money left.

10. There were $3\frac{1}{6}$ loaves of bread on the table.

    After breakfast, there were $1\frac{2}{3}$ loaves left.

    How many loaves of bread were eaten?

    $3\frac{1}{6} - 1\frac{2}{3} = \boxed{\phantom{00}}$

    $\frac{2}{3}$ is greater than $\frac{1}{6}$. So the answer will be between 1 and 2.

    $\boxed{\phantom{00}}$ loaves of bread were eaten.

11. One rope is $12\frac{2}{3}$ feet long and the other is $6\frac{3}{4}$ feet longer.

    The two ropes are tied together so that the final length

    is $1\frac{5}{6}$ feet shorter than if they had been laid side by side.

    What is the total length of the tied ropes?

    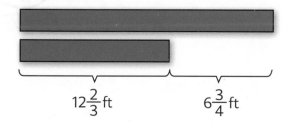

    $12\frac{2}{3}$ ft          $6\frac{3}{4}$ ft

    $12\frac{2}{3} + 12\frac{2}{3} + 6\frac{3}{4} - 1\frac{5}{6} = \boxed{\phantom{00}}$

    The total length of the tied ropes is $\boxed{\phantom{0}}$ feet.

Exercise 7, pages 77–79

# 5 Product of a Fraction and a Whole Number

(a) Monique has 5 pieces of pink lace, each 2 m long.
What is the total length of pink lace that she has?

$5 \times 2 = 10$

She has 10 m of pink lace.

Since 2 is greater than 1, the product is greater than 5.

She has 5 pieces of white lace, each $\frac{1}{2}$ of a meter long.

What is the total length of white lace that she has?

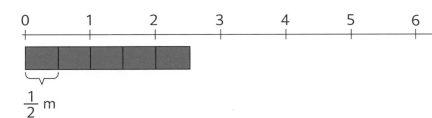

$$\frac{1}{2} m$$

$$\frac{1}{2} + \frac{1}{2} + \frac{1}{2} + \frac{1}{2} + \frac{1}{2} = \frac{5}{2}$$

$$5 \times \frac{1}{2} = \frac{5 \times 1}{2}$$

$$= \frac{5}{2} = \boxed{\phantom{x}}$$

Since $\frac{1}{2}$ is less than 1, the product is smaller than 5.

She has a piece of ribbon that is 5 m long.
How long is $\frac{1}{2}$ of the total length of the ribbon?

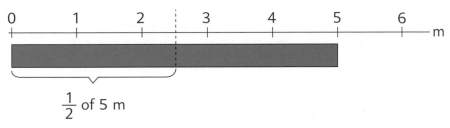

$$\frac{1}{2} \text{ of 5 m}$$

$$\frac{1}{2} \text{ of } 5 = \frac{5}{2} = \boxed{\phantom{x}}$$

$$\frac{1}{2} \times 5 = \frac{1 \times 5}{2}$$

$$= \frac{5}{2} = \boxed{\phantom{x}}$$

77

(b)  Andy has a hall rug that measures 5 m by $\frac{1}{2}$ m.
What is the area of the rug?

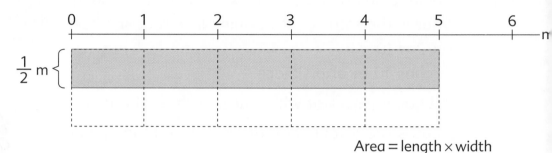

Area = length × width

$$5\,m \times \frac{1}{2}m = \frac{5}{2}m^2$$

$$= \boxed{\phantom{0}}\,m^2$$

(c)  Shayla has 5 spools of thread.
She uses $\frac{1}{2}$ of them to sew a dress.
How many spools of thread did she use?

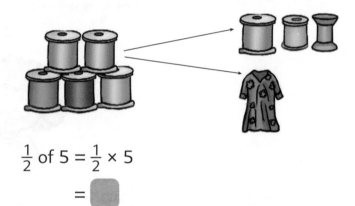

$$\frac{1}{2} \text{ of } 5 = \frac{1}{2} \times 5$$

$$= \boxed{\phantom{0}}$$

Shayla used $\boxed{\phantom{0}}$ spools of thread.

How many spools of thread would she need for 3 dresses,
if she needed the same amount of thread for each?

1. Find the product of $\frac{2}{3}$ and 4.

**Method 1:**

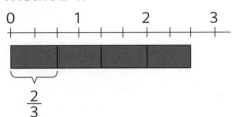

$$4 \times \frac{2}{3} = \frac{4 \times 2}{3}$$

$$= \frac{8}{3} = \boxed{\phantom{x}}$$

**Method 2:**

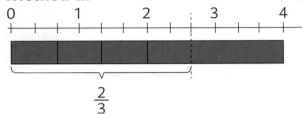

$$\frac{1}{3} \times 4 = \frac{4}{3}$$

$$\frac{2}{3} \times 4 = 2 \times \frac{4}{3}$$

$$= \frac{8}{3}$$

$$= \boxed{\phantom{x}}$$

**Method 3:**

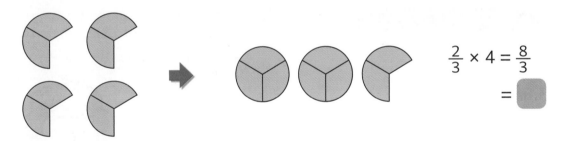

$$\frac{2}{3} \times 4 = \frac{8}{3}$$

$$= \boxed{\phantom{x}}$$

**Method 4:**

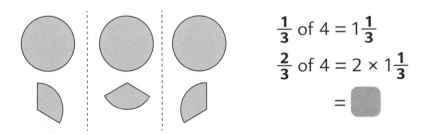

$$\frac{1}{3} \text{ of } 4 = 1\frac{1}{3}$$

$$\frac{2}{3} \text{ of } 4 = 2 \times 1\frac{1}{3}$$

$$= \boxed{\phantom{x}}$$

Write a word problem for each of these methods.

Exercise 8, pages 80–81

2. Lihua bought 12 eggs. She used $\frac{2}{3}$ of them to bake a cake. How many eggs did she use?

**Method 1:**

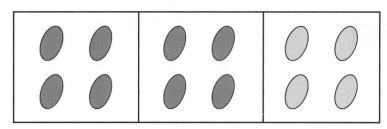

Divide 12 eggs into 3 equal groups. 2 groups are shaded to show $\frac{2}{3}$.

$\frac{2}{3}$ of 12 = ☐

Lihua used ☐ eggs.

**Method 2:**

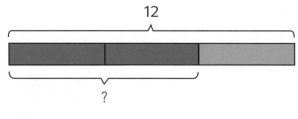

Draw a bar to represent 12 eggs. Divide the bar into 3 equal parts and shade 2 parts to show $\frac{2}{3}$.

3 units = 12

1 unit = ☐

$\frac{2}{3}$ of 12 = 2 units = ☐

Lihua used ☐ eggs.

**Method 3:**

$\frac{2}{3} \times 12 = \frac{2 \times 12}{3}$

$= ☐$

$\frac{2}{3}$ of 12 is the same as $\frac{2}{3} \times 12$.

Lihua used ☐ eggs.

3. Find the value of $\frac{1}{4}$ of 5.

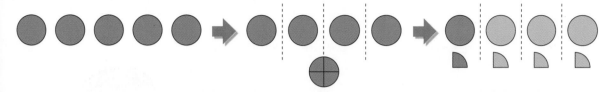

$\frac{1}{4}$ of $5 = 1\frac{1}{4}$

Divide 5 into 4 equal groups. First, one whole goes into each group. There is one whole leftover. I divide it into fourths and put one fourth into each group.

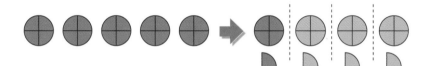

$\frac{1}{4}$ of $5 = \frac{1}{4} \times 5$

$\quad = \frac{1 \times 5}{4}$

$\quad = \frac{5}{4}$

$\quad = 1\frac{1}{4}$

You can also do it in another way. Divide each whole into fourths. There are 20 fourths. You can put 5 fourths into each group.

4. Find the value of $\frac{3}{4}$ of 5.

$\frac{3}{4}$ of $5 = \frac{3}{4} \times 5$

$\quad =$

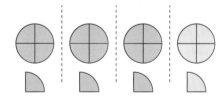

5. Find the value of $\frac{3}{4}$ of 9.

$\frac{3}{4} \times 9 = \frac{3 \times 9}{4}$

$\quad =$

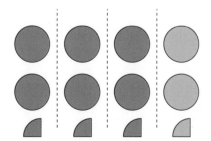

6. (a) Find the value of $\frac{2}{3}$ of 5.

$$\frac{2}{3} \times 5 = \frac{2 \times 5}{3}$$
$$= \boxed{\phantom{0}}$$

$$\frac{2}{3} \times 5 = 5 \times \frac{2}{3}$$

(b) Multiply 5 by $\frac{2}{3}$.

$$5 \times \frac{2}{3} = \frac{5 \times 2}{3}$$
$$= \boxed{\phantom{0}}$$

7. Find the value of $\frac{3}{8} \times 20$.

**Method 1:**

$$\frac{3}{8} \times 20 = \frac{3 \times 20}{8}$$
$$= \frac{60}{8}$$
$$= \boxed{\phantom{0}}$$

Write $\frac{60}{8}$ in its simplest form.

**Method 2:**

$$\frac{3}{8} \times \cancel{20}^{5} = \frac{3 \times \cancel{20}^{5}}{\cancel{8}_{2}}$$
$$= \frac{3 \times 5}{2}$$
$$= \boxed{\phantom{0}}$$

4 is a common factor of 20 and 8.
Divide 20 and 8 by 4.

**Method 3:**

$$\frac{3}{\cancel{8}_{2}} \times \cancel{20}^{5} = \frac{3 \times 5}{2}$$
$$= \boxed{\phantom{0}}$$

8. Multiply. Give each answer in its simplest form.

(a) $\frac{2}{5} \times 10$  (b) $\frac{5}{6} \times 8$  (c) $\frac{3}{4} \times 18$

(d) $12 \times \frac{3}{4}$  (e) $14 \times \frac{1}{6}$  (f) $20 \times \frac{3}{8}$

(g) $\frac{10}{3} \times 6$  (h) $\frac{12}{5} \times 25$  (i) $\frac{11}{4} \times 10$

(j) $15 \times \frac{7}{3}$  (k) $21 \times \frac{11}{9}$  (l) $16 \times \frac{13}{12}$

9. Find the value of each of the following.

(a) $\frac{1}{4}$ of 80  (b) $\frac{1}{5}$ of 50  (c) $\frac{2}{3}$ of 90

(d) $\frac{1}{3} \times 300$  (e) $\frac{3}{4} \times 400$  (f) $\frac{2}{5} \times 100$

Exercise 9, pages 82–84

10. Mike has 5 pieces of molding that are each $3\frac{3}{4}$ ft long.

(a) What is the total length of molding that he has?
Give your answer in its simplest form.

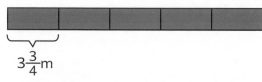

$3\frac{3}{4}$ m

**Method 1:**

$3\frac{3}{4} \times 5$

$3 \quad \frac{3}{4}$

$3 \times 5 = 15$

$\frac{3}{4} \times 5 = \boxed{\phantom{0}}$

$3\frac{3}{4} \times 5 = 15 + \boxed{\phantom{0}} = \boxed{\phantom{0}}$

Since $3\frac{3}{4}$ is greater than 1, the product is greater than 5.

**Method 2:**

$3\frac{3}{4} \times 5 = \frac{15}{4} \times 5$

$= \frac{15 \times 5}{4} = \boxed{\phantom{0}}$

Mike has $\boxed{\phantom{0}}$ ft of molding.

(b) Give the answer in feet and inches.

11. A rectangular rug measures 4 m by $2\frac{2}{3}$ m.
What is the area in meters squared?

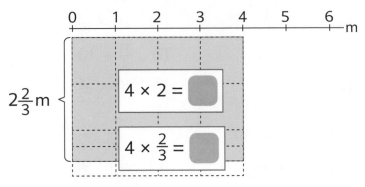

$4 \times 2\frac{2}{3} = 8 +$ ⬚

It has an area of ⬚ m².

12. Find the product of 6 and $2\frac{5}{12}$.

Give the answer in its simplest form.

$6 \times 2\frac{5}{12} = \overset{1}{\cancel{6}} \times \frac{29}{\underset{2}{\cancel{12}}}$

$= \frac{29}{2}$

$=$ ⬚

Change the mixed number to an improper fraction and then multiply.

13. Multiply. Give each answer in its simplest form.

(a) $4\frac{3}{4} \times 12$

(b) $2\frac{2}{5} \times 10$

(c) $9 \times 2\frac{2}{3}$

(d) $3\frac{3}{4} \times 7$

(e) $1\frac{3}{10} \times 15$

(f) $6 \times 4\frac{5}{8}$

Exercise 10, pages 85—86

# 6 Word Problems

Melissa had $125.

She spent $\frac{2}{5}$ of the money and saved the rest.

How much money did she save?

**Method 1:**

$1 - \frac{2}{5} = \frac{3}{5}$

She saved $\frac{3}{5}$ of the money.

First, find what fraction of the money is saved.

$\frac{3}{5} \times \$125 = \$\boxed{\phantom{00}}$

Melissa saved $\$\boxed{\phantom{00}}$.

**Method 2:**

Amount of money spent $= \frac{2}{\cancel{5}^{1}} \times \cancel{\$125}^{25} = \$50$

Amount of money saved $= \$125 - \$50 = \$\boxed{\phantom{00}}$

Here is another way.

**Method 3:**

$125

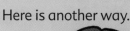

5 units $= \$125$

1 unit $= \$\boxed{\phantom{00}}$

Amount of money saved $= 3$ units $= \$\boxed{\phantom{00}}$

Here is yet another way. I find 1 unit first.

1. There are 96 children in a library.

   Of them, $\frac{5}{8}$ are girls.

   How many boys are there?

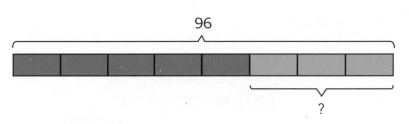

8 units = 96
3 units = ?

2. David had $40.
   He spent $\frac{1}{5}$ of the money on a storybook and $\frac{3}{10}$ on a calculator.
   How much did he spend altogether?

10 units = 40

5 units = ?

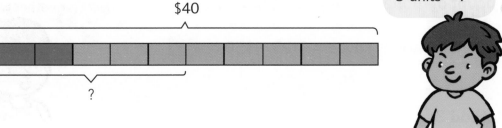

3. Scott had some eggs.
   He sold $\frac{5}{8}$ of them.

   If he sold 300 eggs, how
   many eggs did he have at first?

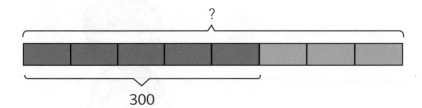

4. Mrs. Garcia brought 6 pies to a picnic.

   Of the pies, $\frac{3}{5}$ were eaten.

   How many pies were left?

   $$\left(1 - \frac{3}{5}\right) \times 6 = \boxed{\phantom{0}}$$

   There were $\boxed{\phantom{0}}$ pies left.

5. Josh has 8 lengths of rain gutter each $12\frac{1}{3}$ ft long.
   What is the total length in feet of rain gutter he has?

   $$8 \times 12\frac{1}{3} = \boxed{\phantom{0}}$$

   He has $\boxed{\phantom{0}}$ feet of rain gutter.

6. There were 6 cakes at a picnic. Of them, $\frac{1}{2}$ had chocolate frosting,
   $\frac{1}{3}$ had vanilla frosting, and the rest had strawberry frosting.

   If $\frac{2}{3}$ of the cakes with chocolate frosting and $\frac{3}{4}$ of the cakes with vanilla
   frosting were eaten, how many cakes were left?

   $$6 - \left(\frac{2}{3} \times 3\right) - \left(\frac{3}{4} \times 2\right) = \boxed{\phantom{0}}$$

   There were $\boxed{\phantom{0}}$ cakes left.

Exercise 11, pages 87–91

1. This figure is made up of rectangles of the same shape and size. What fraction of the figure is shaded?

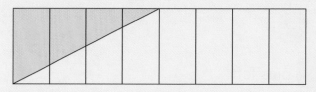

   (A) $\frac{1}{2}$      (B) $\frac{1}{4}$      (C) $\frac{1}{3}$      (D) $\frac{4}{5}$

2. Which one of the following is arranged in descending order?

   (A) $\frac{5}{8}, \frac{1}{2}, \frac{1}{4}$          (B) $\frac{1}{2}, \frac{1}{8}, \frac{1}{4}$

   (C) $\frac{1}{2}, \frac{1}{4}, \frac{5}{8}$          (D) $\frac{1}{4}, \frac{1}{2}, \frac{5}{8}$

3. The difference between two numbers is one third of their sum. Which of the following could be the two numbers?

   (A) 10 and 15          (B) 20 and 15

   (C) 15 and 30          (D) 25 and 75

4. How many times can you subtract $\frac{1}{8}$ from 3?

   (A) $\frac{1}{5}$      (B) 3      (C) 24      (D) 30

5. Select True or False.

   (a) $\frac{28}{98}$ in its simplest form is $\frac{2}{7}$.      True / False

   (b) If $\frac{1}{3}$ of a number is 12, then $\frac{1}{2}$ of the number is 20.      True / False

6. Select True or False.

   (a) $4 - 1\frac{1}{8} + 1\frac{1}{2} \times 6 = 37$      True / False

   (b) $\frac{2}{3}$ of 64 is 25.      True / False

7. Write the fractions represented by A, B, and C in their simplest form.

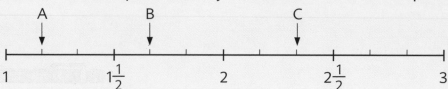

8. Express each fraction in its simplest form.

   (a) $\frac{6}{8}$        (b) $\frac{9}{15}$        (c) $\frac{16}{24}$        (d) $\frac{32}{40}$

9. Express each fraction as an improper fraction.

   (a) $4\frac{5}{9}$        (b) $2\frac{3}{4}$        (c) $5\frac{3}{8}$        (d) $3\frac{7}{11}$

10. Express each fraction as a whole number or a mixed number in its simplest form.

   (a) $\frac{20}{6}$        (b) $\frac{16}{4}$        (c) $\frac{33}{3}$        (d) $\frac{30}{8}$

11. Name two equivalent fractions for each of these fractions.

   (a) $\frac{3}{4}$        (b) $\frac{2}{6}$        (c) $\frac{5}{9}$        (d) $\frac{11}{14}$

12. Divide. Express each answer as a fraction in its simplest form.

   (a)  $8 \div 12$                        (b) $15 \div 54$
   (c)  $63 \div 18$                       (d) $100 \div 35$

13. Which is greater?

   (a) $\frac{3}{2}$ or $\frac{5}{4}$        (b) $2\frac{1}{2}$ or $2\frac{1}{7}$        (c) $3\frac{8}{9}$ or 4

   (d) $1\frac{6}{7}$ or $\frac{12}{7}$        (e) $4\frac{2}{3}$ or $\frac{9}{2}$        (f) $3\frac{1}{6}$ or $\frac{16}{5}$

14. Arrange the fractions in order, beginning with the smallest.

   (a) $1\frac{3}{4}$, $\frac{9}{4}$, $1\frac{5}{8}$, $\frac{9}{2}$              (b) $1\frac{2}{8}$, $\frac{36}{5}$, $1\frac{2}{3}$, $\frac{8}{2}$

15. What number must be added to $4\frac{2}{9}$ to make 5?

16. Add or subtract. Give each answer in its simplest form.

   (a) $\frac{5}{6} + \frac{3}{4}$        (b) $2\frac{1}{2} + 5\frac{4}{5}$        (c) $4\frac{3}{4} - \frac{2}{3}$

   (d) $3\frac{3}{8} + \frac{5}{12}$        (e) $6 - \frac{6}{7}$        (f) $6\frac{1}{3} - 2\frac{3}{5}$

   (g) $7\frac{3}{5} - 2\frac{1}{4}$        (h) $6\frac{1}{3} + 8\frac{3}{5}$        (i) $\frac{2}{3} + \frac{4}{9}$

17. Multiply.

   (a) $\frac{7}{20} \times 4$      (b) $24 \times \frac{5}{8}$      (c) $35 \times \frac{2}{5}$

   (d) $15 \times \frac{5}{6}$      (e) $9 \times \frac{5}{12}$      (f) $7 \times \frac{7}{10}$

   (g) $4 \times 2\frac{2}{3}$      (h) $6\frac{7}{8} \times 3$      (i) $3\frac{2}{5} \times 100$

18. Divide. Express each answer as a whole number or fraction in simplest form.

   (a) $45 \div 7$      (b) $345 \div 8$      (c) $4{,}502 \div 6$

   (d) $36 \div 21$      (e) $3{,}605 \div 15$      (f) $10{,}008 \div 26$

19. Add or subtract.

   (a) $\frac{5}{6} + \frac{7}{10}$   (b) $3\frac{4}{9} - \frac{7}{8}$   (c) $5\frac{1}{3} + 6\frac{5}{12}$   (d) $7\frac{1}{7} - 2\frac{4}{6}$

20. Bonita bought $2\frac{1}{5}$ kg of potatoes and $1\frac{1}{2}$ kg of carrots.
    How many more potatoes than carrots did she buy?

21. There are 42 students in Miss Brown's class.
    Of them, $\frac{3}{7}$ wear glasses.
    How many students wear glasses?

22. Danny bought 6 cartons of drink.
    Each carton contained $\frac{1}{4}$ L of drink.
    Find the total amount of drink in liters.

23. Lynn bought 8 m of string.
    She used $\frac{5}{8}$ of the string to make a flower pot hanger.
    How much of the string did she have left?

24. Matthew had 64 watermelons.
    He sold $\frac{3}{4}$ of them.
    How many watermelons did he sell?

25. Mrs. Gray had 2 kg of flour.
    She used $\frac{2}{5}$ of it to make buns.
    How much flour did she have left?
    Give the answer in kilograms.

26. What number is exactly halfway between $\frac{1}{5}$ and $\frac{5}{7}$?
    Explain how you found the answer.

Review 3, pages 92—96

# 4 MULTIPLY AND DIVIDE FRACTIONS

## 1 Product of Fractions

Color $\frac{3}{4}$ of a rectangle.

Cut out $\frac{1}{2}$ of the colored parts.

What fraction of the rectangle is cut out?

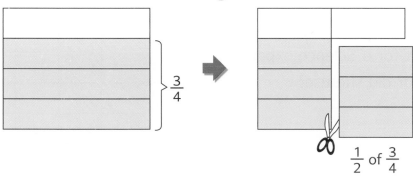

$\frac{1}{2}$ of $\frac{3}{4}$

$\frac{1}{2}$ of $\frac{3}{4} = \frac{3}{8}$

$\frac{3}{8}$ of the rectangle is cut out.

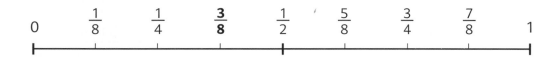

$\frac{1}{2}$ of $\frac{3}{4}$

We can write $\frac{1}{2}$ of $\frac{3}{4}$ as $\frac{1}{2} \times \frac{3}{4}$.

$$\frac{1}{2} \times \frac{3}{4} = \frac{3}{4} \times \frac{1}{2}$$

$$\frac{1}{2} \times \frac{3}{4} = \frac{1 \times 3}{2 \times 4}$$
$$= \frac{3}{8}$$

Is the product of two fractions that are both less than 1 greater than or less than either of the factors?

1. A flower garden occupies $\frac{1}{2}$ of a piece of land. Of the garden, $\frac{3}{5}$ is used for growing orchids. What fraction of the land is used for growing orchids?

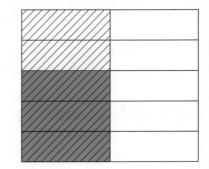

   $\frac{3}{5} \times \frac{1}{2} = $ ⬜

   ⬜ of the land is used for growing orchids.

2. Mrs. Green bought $\frac{3}{5}$ lb of sugar. She used $\frac{3}{4}$ of it for a Science experiment. How much sugar did she use?

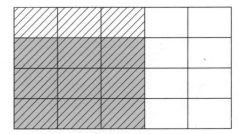

   $\frac{3}{4} \times \frac{3}{5} = $ ⬜

   Mrs. Green used ⬜ lb of sugar.

3. In a classroom, $\frac{2}{3}$ of a wall is painted red.

   Of the remaining part, $\frac{1}{4}$ is painted gray. What fraction of the wall is painted gray?

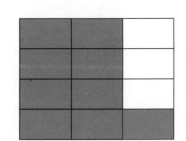

   $1 - \frac{2}{3} = \frac{1}{3}$

   The remaining part is $\frac{1}{3}$ of the wall.

   $\frac{1}{4} \times \frac{1}{3} = $ ⬜

   ⬜ of the wall is painted gray.

4. Sally ate $\frac{1}{6}$ of a fruit pie and gave $\frac{1}{5}$ of the remainder to her sister.
What fraction of the fruit pie did she give away?

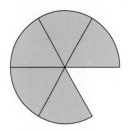

$\frac{1}{5} \times \frac{5}{6} =$

Sally gave away ⬜ of the pie.

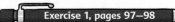
Exercise 1, pages 97–98

5. Multiply $\frac{4}{5}$ by $\frac{2}{3}$.

$\frac{4}{5} \times \frac{2}{3} = \frac{4 \times 2}{5 \times 3}$

$= ⬜$

6. Find the product of $\frac{9}{10}$ and $\frac{5}{12}$.

**Method 1:**

$\frac{9}{10} \times \frac{5}{12} = \frac{{}^3\cancel{9} \times \cancel{5}^{\,1}}{{}_2\cancel{10} \times \cancel{12}_4}$

$= ⬜$

**Method 2:**

$\frac{{}^3\cancel{9}}{{}_2\cancel{10}} \times \frac{\cancel{5}^{\,1}}{\cancel{12}_4} = \frac{3 \times 1}{2 \times 4}$

$= ⬜$

7. Find the value of each of the following.

(a) $\frac{1}{2}$ of $\frac{1}{2}$

(b) $\frac{1}{3}$ of $\frac{3}{4}$

(c) $\frac{1}{4}$ of $\frac{8}{9}$

(d) $\frac{5}{6} \times \frac{1}{5}$

(e) $\frac{3}{4} \times \frac{5}{6}$

(f) $\frac{4}{5} \times \frac{3}{8}$

(g) $\frac{5}{8} \times \frac{4}{9}$

(h) $\frac{1}{3} \times \frac{6}{7}$

(i) $\frac{5}{6} \times \frac{7}{10}$

(j) $\frac{15}{4} \times \frac{8}{3}$

(k) $\frac{9}{4} \times \frac{16}{3}$

(l) $\frac{12}{5} \times \frac{20}{9}$

Exercise 2, page 99

8. Multiply $3\frac{1}{3} \times 2\frac{5}{8}$.

The answer will be between $3 \times 2$ and $4 \times 3$.

$3\frac{1}{3} \times 2\frac{5}{8}$

$= 3 \times 2 + 3 \times \frac{5}{8} + \frac{1}{3} \times 2 + \frac{1}{3} \times \frac{5}{8}$

$= \quad 6 \quad + \square + \square + \square$

$= \square$

$3\frac{1}{3} \times 2\frac{5}{8} = \frac{10}{3} \times \frac{21}{8}$

Convert to improper fractions.

$= \frac{\square}{24}$

$= \square$

9. Find the value of each of the following.

(a) $3\frac{3}{4} \times 2\frac{2}{3}$

(b) $2\frac{1}{4} \times 5\frac{1}{3}$

(c) $2\frac{2}{5} \times 3\frac{2}{9}$

(d) $5\frac{1}{2} \times 4\frac{5}{6}$

(e) $\frac{3}{4} \times 3\frac{1}{4}$

(f) $4\frac{3}{10} \times \frac{1}{2}$

(g) $2\frac{5}{12} \times 8\frac{5}{6}$

(h) $7\frac{2}{9} \times 5\frac{2}{5}$

(i) $2\frac{7}{10} \times 3\frac{7}{9}$

Exercise 3, pages 100–101

## 2 Word Problems

Jim had 360 stamps. He sold $\frac{1}{3}$ of them on Monday and $\frac{1}{4}$ of the remainder on Tuesday. How many stamps did he sell on Tuesday?

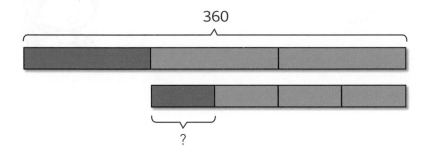

360

?

**Method 1:**

$1 - \frac{1}{3} = \frac{2}{3}$

First, find what fraction of the stamps were left on Monday.

He had $\frac{2}{3}$ of the stamps left on Monday.
The remainder is $\frac{2}{3}$.

$$\frac{1}{\underset{2}{\cancel{4}}} \times \frac{\overset{1}{\cancel{2}}}{3} = \frac{1}{2 \times 3}$$
$$= \frac{1}{6}$$

Next, find $\frac{1}{4}$ of the remainder.

He sold $\frac{1}{6}$ of the stamps on Tuesday.

$\frac{1}{6} \times 360 = \boxed{\phantom{00}}$

Jim sold $\boxed{\phantom{0}}$ stamps on Tuesday.

**Method 2:**

$1 - \frac{1}{3} = \frac{2}{3}$

He had $\frac{2}{3}$ of the stamps left on Monday.

$\frac{2}{\cancel{3}_1} \times \cancel{360}^{120} = 2 \times 120 = 240$

He had 240 stamps left on Monday.

$\frac{1}{4} \times 240 = $

Jim sold [ ] stamps on Tuesday.

Find the number of stamps left on Monday.

**Method 3:**

$\frac{1}{\cancel{3}_1} \times \cancel{360}^{120} = 120$

He sold 120 stamps on Monday.

$360 - 120 = 240$

He had 240 stamps left on Monday.

$\frac{1}{4} \times 240 = $ [ ]

Jim sold [ ] stamps on Tuesday.

Find the number of stamps he sold on Monday first.

I divide all the units into 2 parts, so there are now 6 parts.

**Method 4:**

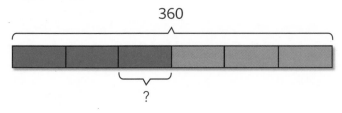

Total number of stamps = 6 units = 360

Number of stamps sold on Tuesday = 1 unit = [ ]

1. Marisol made 300 tarts. She sold $\frac{3}{4}$ of them and gave $\frac{1}{3}$ of the remainder to her neighbor. How many tarts did she have left?

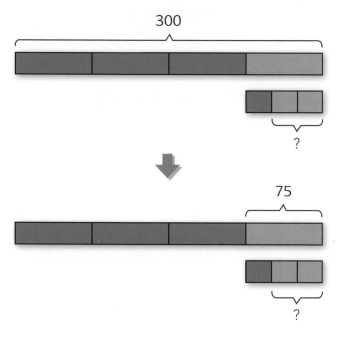

2. Mr. Anderson gave $\frac{2}{5}$ of his money to his wife and spent $\frac{1}{2}$ of the remainder. If he had $300 left, how much money did he have at first?

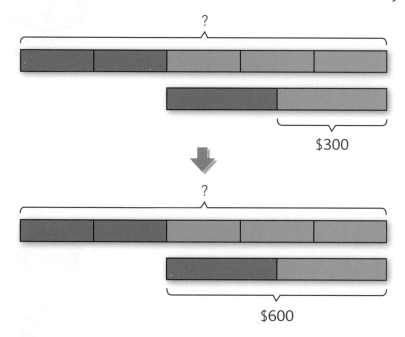

Exercise 4, pages 102–105

3. Shawn had a piece of string $4\frac{1}{2}$ m long.

   He used $\frac{1}{3}$ of it to tie a box.

   Find the length of the string that was used to tie the box.

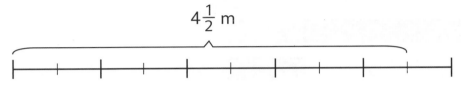

$4\frac{1}{2}$ m

**Method 1:**

There are 9 half-meters in $4\frac{1}{2}$ m.

$\frac{1}{3}$ of them are 3 half-meters.

$3 \times \frac{1}{2} = 1\frac{1}{2}$

Which method is more efficient? What if his piece of string was $3\frac{3}{4}$ m long instead?

**Method 2:**

$\frac{1}{3} \times 4\frac{1}{2} = \boxed{\phantom{00}}$

4. Kelley had $2\frac{3}{4}$ qt of cooking oil.

   She used $\frac{2}{5}$ of it to deep-fry some fish.

   How much oil did she use?

   $\frac{2}{5} \times 2\frac{3}{4} = \boxed{\phantom{00}}$

$\frac{2}{5}$ is smaller than $\frac{1}{2}$. $\frac{1}{2}$ of 2 is 1 and $\frac{1}{2}$ of $\frac{3}{4}$ is less than $\frac{1}{2}$. The answer will be between 1 and 2.

Exercise 5, pages 106—109

# ③ Dividing a Fraction by a Whole Number

2 boys shared $\frac{1}{3}$ of a pizza equally.

What fraction of the pizza did each boy receive?

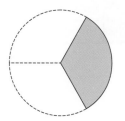 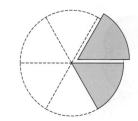

$$\frac{1}{3} \div 2 = \frac{1}{6}$$

Each boy received $\frac{1}{6}$ of the pizza.

| 0 | $\frac{1}{6}$ | $\frac{1}{3}$ | $\frac{1}{2}$ | $\frac{2}{3}$ | $\frac{5}{6}$ | 1 |

$\frac{1}{2}$ of $\frac{1}{3}$

$\frac{1}{3} \times \frac{1}{2} = \frac{1}{2} \times \frac{1}{3}$

$\frac{1}{3} \div 2 = \frac{1}{2}$ of $\frac{1}{3}$

$\phantom{\frac{1}{3} \div 2} = \frac{1}{2} \times \frac{1}{3}$

$\phantom{\frac{1}{3} \div 2} = \boxed{\phantom{x}}$

Divide $\frac{1}{3}$ by 2.

$\frac{1}{3} \div 2 = \frac{1}{2} \times \frac{1}{3}$

$\phantom{\frac{1}{3} \div 2} = \boxed{\phantom{x}}$

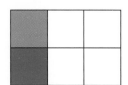

Check: $\boxed{\phantom{x}} \times 2 = \frac{1}{3}$

1. Divide $\frac{1}{4}$ by 5.

$$\frac{1}{4} \div 5 = \frac{1}{4} \times \frac{1}{5}$$

$$= \boxed{\phantom{0}}$$

Dividing by 5 is the same as multiplying by $\frac{1}{5}$.

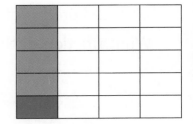

2. Divide. Make up a word problem for each situation.

(a) $\frac{1}{4} \div 6 = \frac{1}{4} \times \frac{1}{6}$

$$= \boxed{\phantom{0}}$$

(b) $\frac{1}{5} \div 9 = \frac{1}{5} \times \frac{1}{9}$

$$= \boxed{\phantom{0}}$$

(c) $\frac{1}{6} \div 5 = \frac{1}{6} \times \boxed{\phantom{0}}$

$$= \boxed{\phantom{0}}$$

(d) $\frac{1}{10} \div 3 = \frac{1}{10} \times \boxed{\phantom{0}}$

$$= \boxed{\phantom{0}}$$

3. Find the value of each of the following in its simplest form.

(a) $\frac{1}{3} \div 2$

(b) $\frac{1}{5} \div 3$

(c) $\frac{1}{7} \div 4$

(d) $\frac{1}{5} \div 4$

(e) $\frac{1}{7} \div 2$

(f) $\frac{1}{3} \div 8$

(g) $\frac{1}{10} \div 6$

(h) $\frac{1}{8} \div 6$

Exercise 6, pages 110–111

4. 4 boys shared $\frac{2}{3}$ of a pizza equally.

What fraction of the pizza did each boy receive?

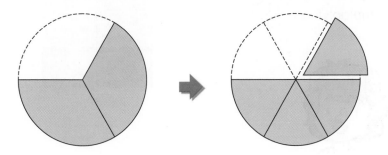

$\frac{2}{3} \div 4 = \frac{1}{6}$

Each boy received $\frac{1}{6}$ of the pizza.

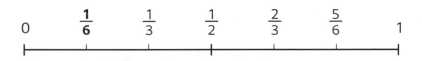

$\frac{1}{4}$ of $\frac{2}{3}$

$\frac{2}{3} \times \frac{1}{4} = \frac{1}{4} \times \frac{2}{3}$

$\frac{2}{3} \div 4 = \frac{1}{4}$ of $\frac{2}{3}$  or  $\frac{2}{3} \div 4 = \frac{\overset{1}{\cancel{2}}}{3} \times \frac{1}{\underset{2}{\cancel{4}}}$

$\quad\quad\quad = \frac{1}{\underset{2}{\cancel{4}}} \times \frac{\overset{1}{\cancel{2}}}{3}$ $\quad\quad\quad\quad\quad = \frac{1}{6}$

$\quad\quad\quad = \frac{1}{6}$

Check: $\frac{1}{6} \times 4 = $ ⬜

101

5. Divide $\frac{2}{3}$ by 3.

$\frac{2}{3} \div 3 = \frac{2}{3} \times \frac{1}{3}$

$= \boxed{\phantom{0}}$

Dividing by 3 is the same as multiplying by $\frac{1}{3}$.

6. Divide.

(a) $\frac{3}{4} \div 6 = \frac{3}{4} \times \frac{1}{6}$

$= \boxed{\phantom{0}}$

(b) $\frac{3}{5} \div 9 = \frac{3}{5} \times \frac{1}{9}$

$= \boxed{\phantom{0}}$

(c) $\frac{5}{6} \div 5 = \frac{5}{6} \times \boxed{\phantom{0}}$

$= \boxed{\phantom{0}}$

(d) $\frac{9}{10} \div 3 = \frac{9}{10} \times \boxed{\phantom{0}}$

$= \boxed{\phantom{0}}$

7. Find the value of each of the following in its simplest form.

(a) $\frac{2}{3} \div 2$

(b) $\frac{4}{5} \div 3$

(c) $\frac{5}{7} \div 4$

(d) $\frac{4}{5} \div 4$

(e) $\frac{6}{7} \div 2$

(f) $\frac{2}{3} \div 8$

(g) $\frac{9}{16} \div 3$

(h) $\frac{3}{8} \div 6$

(i) $\frac{9}{10} \div 6$

(j) $\frac{4}{9} \div 8$

Exercise 7, pages 112–116

# ④ Dividing by a Fraction

Andrea bought 3 oranges.
She cut each orange into halves.
How many pieces of orange did she have?

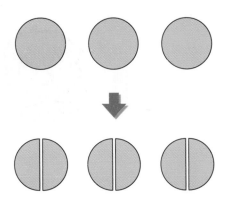

There are 2 halves in 1 whole.
There are 6 halves in 3 wholes.

$3 \div \frac{1}{2} = 6$

She had 6 pieces of orange.

$3 \div \frac{1}{2} = 3 \times 2$
$\qquad = 6$

Dividing by $\frac{1}{2}$ is the same
as multiplying by 2.

2 is the reciprocal of $\frac{1}{2}$.

Check: $6 \times \frac{1}{2} = \boxed{\phantom{0}}$

1. How many bricks weighing $\frac{1}{4}$ lb each will have a total weight of 3 lb?

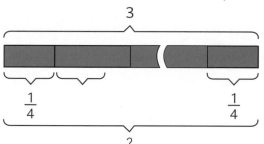

How many $\frac{1}{4}$ are there in 3?

$\frac{1}{4} \times ? = 3.$

Write a division expression for this problem:

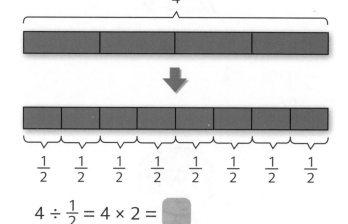

 $\frac{1}{4}$-lb bricks weigh 3 lb.

2. How many pieces of ribbon, each $\frac{1}{2}$ m long, can be cut from a ribbon that is 4 m long?

How many $\frac{1}{2}$'s can be made from 4 wholes?

$\frac{1}{2} \times \boxed{\phantom{0}} = 4$

$4 \div \frac{1}{2} = 4 \times 2 = \boxed{\phantom{0}}$

Dividing by $\frac{1}{2}$ is the same as multiplying by 2.

2 is the reciprocal of $\boxed{\phantom{0}}$.

3.  (a)  Divide 2 by $\frac{1}{3}$.

$2 \div \frac{1}{3} = 2 \times 3$

$\quad\quad = \square$

How many thirds are there in 2 wholes?

(b)  Make up a problem that can be solved by dividing 2 by $\frac{1}{3}$.

4.  Divide. Make up a word problem for each situation.

(a)  $1 \div \frac{1}{4} = 1 \times \square$

$\quad\quad = \square$

(b)  $2 \div \frac{1}{5} = 2 \times \square$

$\quad\quad = \square$

5.  Divide.

(a)  $4 \div \frac{1}{2}$          (b)  $6 \div \frac{1}{6}$

(c)  $3 \div \frac{1}{7}$          (d)  $8 \div \frac{1}{4}$

(e)  $5 \div \frac{1}{3}$          (f)  $9 \div \frac{1}{9}$

(g)  $3 \div \frac{1}{2}$          (h)  $5 \div \frac{1}{4}$

(i)  $6 \div \frac{2}{3}$

Exercise 8, pages 117–119

6.  Divide $\frac{1}{2}$ by $\frac{1}{4}$.

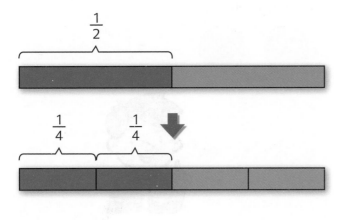

Divide $\frac{1}{2}$ into fourths.
There are 2 fourths.

$\frac{1}{2} \div \frac{1}{4} = \frac{1}{2} \times 4$

$= \boxed{\phantom{0}}$

Dividing by $\frac{1}{4}$ is the same as multiplying by 4.

4 is the reciprocal of $\frac{1}{4}$.

7.  A beaker has $\frac{4}{5}$ L of solution. All of it is poured into test tubes.
    Each test tube needs $\frac{1}{10}$ L of solution. How many test tubes are used?

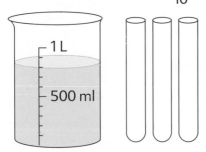

$\frac{4}{5} \div \frac{1}{10} = \frac{4}{5} \times 10$

$= \boxed{\phantom{0}}$

Check: $\boxed{\phantom{0}} \times \frac{1}{10} = \frac{4}{5}$

8. Divide.

(a) $\frac{2}{3} \div \frac{1}{3} = \frac{2}{3} \times$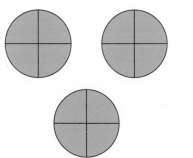

$=$

(b) $\frac{2}{3} \div \frac{1}{6} = \frac{2}{3} \times$

$=$

9. Divide.

(a) $\frac{1}{4} \div \frac{1}{2}$

(b) $\frac{2}{5} \div \frac{1}{10}$

(c) $\frac{3}{4} \div \frac{1}{8}$

(d) $\frac{5}{6} \div \frac{1}{6}$

(e) $\frac{2}{9} \div \frac{1}{3}$

(f) $\frac{3}{8} \div \frac{1}{4}$

Exercise 9, page 120

10. Divide 3 by $\frac{3}{4}$.

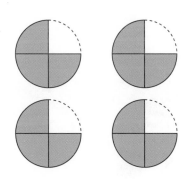

$3 \div \frac{3}{4} = 3 \times \frac{4}{3}$

$=$

How many $\frac{3}{4}$'s can be made from 3 wholes?

Dividing by $\frac{3}{4}$ is the same as multiplying by $\frac{4}{3}$.

$\frac{4}{3}$ is the reciprocal of $\frac{3}{4}$.

11. Nicole used 6 m of string to tie some packages.
    She used $\frac{2}{3}$ m of string for each package.
    How many packages did she tie?

6 m

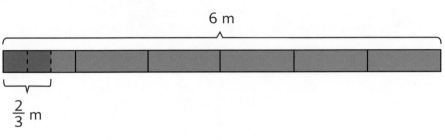

$\frac{2}{3}$ m

$6 \div \frac{2}{3} = 6 \times$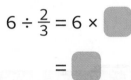

$=$ □

Check: □ $\times \frac{2}{3} = 6$

12. Divide.

    (a) $3 \div \frac{3}{8} = 3 \times$ □

    $=$ □

    (b) $8 \div \frac{4}{5} = 8 \times$ □

    $=$ □

13. Divide.

    (a) $2 \div \frac{2}{3}$          (b) $5 \div \frac{5}{6}$

    (c) $6 \div \frac{3}{5}$          (d) $8 \div \frac{4}{5}$

    (e) $6 \div \frac{6}{7}$          (f) $9 \div \frac{3}{4}$

Exercise 10, page 121

14. Divide $\frac{3}{4}$ by $\frac{3}{8}$.

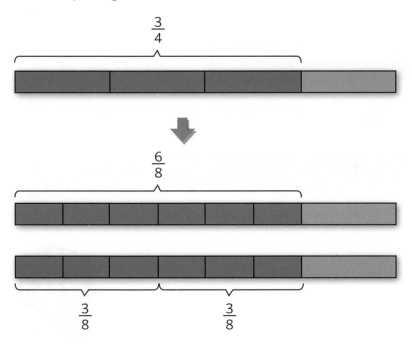

$\frac{3}{4}$

$\frac{6}{8}$

$\frac{3}{8}$  $\frac{3}{8}$

How many $\frac{3}{8}$'s are there in $\frac{3}{4}$?

There are two $\frac{3}{8}$'s in $\frac{3}{4}$.

$$\frac{3}{4} \div \frac{3}{8} = \frac{3}{\underset{1}{4}} \times \frac{\overset{2}{8}}{3}$$

$$= \boxed{\phantom{0}}$$

Dividing by $\frac{3}{8}$ is the same as multiplying by $\frac{8}{3}$.

$\frac{8}{3}$ is the reciprocal of $\frac{3}{8}$.

15. Divide.

(a)  $\frac{2}{3} \div \frac{2}{9}$

(b)  $\frac{3}{5} \div \frac{3}{10}$

(c)  $\frac{2}{5} \div \frac{2}{10}$

(d)  $\frac{1}{3} \div \frac{1}{9}$

16. Divide 3 by $\frac{2}{3}$.

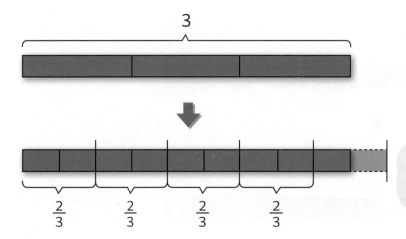

How many $\frac{2}{3}$'s can be made from 3 wholes?

There are four $\frac{2}{3}$'s, and another half of a $\frac{2}{3}$ in 3.

So there are four-and-a-half $\frac{2}{3}$'s in 3.

$3 \div \frac{2}{3} = 3 \times \frac{3}{2}$

$\qquad = \frac{\blacksquare}{\blacksquare}$

$\qquad = 4\frac{\blacksquare}{\blacksquare}$

Dividing by $\frac{2}{3}$ is the same as multiplying by $\frac{3}{2}$.

$\frac{3}{2}$ is the reciprocal of $\frac{2}{3}$.

17. Divide.

   (a)  $2 \div \frac{3}{5}$        (b)  $5 \div \frac{3}{4}$

   (c)  $3 \div \frac{2}{5}$        (d)  $6 \div \frac{5}{6}$

18. Divide $\frac{3}{4}$ by $\frac{5}{8}$.

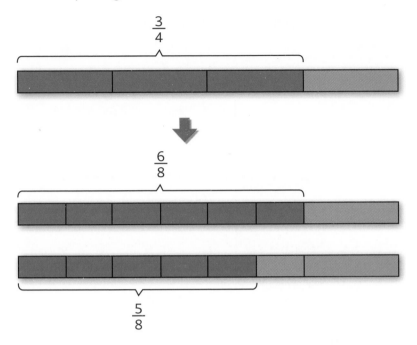

How many $\frac{5}{8}$'s are there in $\frac{3}{4}$?

There is one $\frac{5}{8}$ and one fifth of another $\frac{5}{8}$ in $\frac{3}{4}$.

There are one and one fifth $\frac{5}{8}$'s in $\frac{3}{4}$.

$$\frac{3}{4} \div \frac{5}{8} = \frac{3}{{}_14\!\!\!\!/} \times \frac{8\!\!\!\!/^2}{5}$$

$$= \frac{\square}{\square} = 1\frac{\square}{\square}$$

Dividing by $\frac{5}{8}$ is the same as multiplying by $\frac{8}{5}$.

$\frac{8}{5}$ is the reciprocal of $\frac{5}{8}$.

19. Divide.

(a) $\frac{1}{3} \div \frac{2}{9} = \frac{1}{3} \times \boxed{\phantom{x}}$

$= \boxed{\phantom{x}}$

(b) $\frac{5}{6} \div \frac{2}{3} = \frac{5}{6} \times \boxed{\phantom{x}}$

$= \boxed{\phantom{x}}$

20. Divide.

(a) $\frac{2}{3} \div \frac{3}{5}$

(b) $\frac{3}{5} \div \frac{9}{10}$

(c) $\frac{5}{8} \div \frac{2}{5}$

Exercise 11, page 122

# 5 More Word Problems

A tank is $\frac{1}{5}$ full. When another 700 ml of water is poured into the tank, it becomes $\frac{2}{3}$ full.

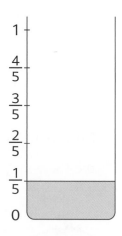 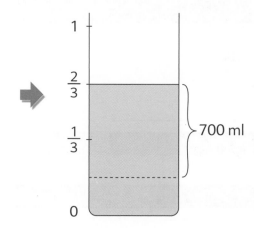

$$\frac{2}{3} - \frac{1}{5} = \frac{10}{15} - \frac{3}{15}$$
$$= \frac{7}{15}$$

700 ml fills $\frac{7}{15}$ of the tank.

$\frac{7}{15}$ ⟶ 700 ml

How much water is in the tank when it is $\frac{1}{5}$ full?

$\frac{1}{5}$ ⟶ ⬜ ml

How much water is in the tank when it is $\frac{2}{3}$ full?

$\frac{2}{3}$ ⟶ ⬜ ml

1.  Alex bought some chairs. Of them, $\frac{1}{3}$ were red and $\frac{1}{4}$ were blue.
    The remaining 35 chairs were yellow.
    (a)  What fraction of the chairs were yellow?

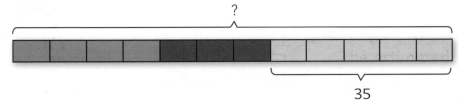

(b)  How many chairs did Alex buy?

?

35

**Method 1:**

5 units = 35

1 unit = $\frac{35}{5}$ = 7

12 units = 7 × 12

= 

**Method 2:**

$\frac{5}{12}$ ⟶ 35

$\frac{1}{12}$ ⟶ $\frac{35}{5}$ = 7

$\frac{12}{12}$ ⟶ 7 × 12 = 

**Method 3:**

$\frac{5}{12}$ of what is 35?

$35 \div \frac{5}{12} = 35 \times \frac{12}{5}$

=

2. Max spent $\frac{3}{5}$ of his money in a shop and $\frac{1}{4}$ of the remainder in another shop.

(a) What fraction of his money was left?

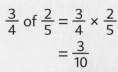

$$\frac{3}{4} \text{ of } \frac{2}{5} = \frac{3}{4} \times \frac{2}{5}$$
$$= \frac{3}{10}$$

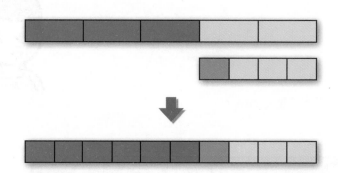

(b) If he had $90 left, how much money did he have at first?

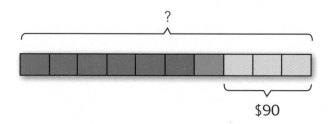

3. Sam withdrew $\frac{3}{4}$ of his savings from the bank.
He spent $450 of it and had $150 left.
How much was the total savings in the bank at first?

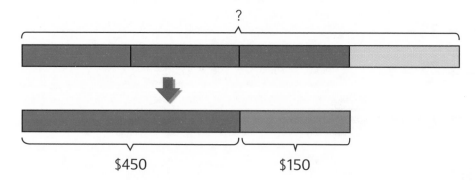

Exercise 12, pages 123–127

4. Lindsey read $\frac{2}{5}$ of a book on Monday.

   She read 12 pages on Tuesday.

   If she still had $\frac{1}{2}$ of the book to read, how many pages
   were there in the book?

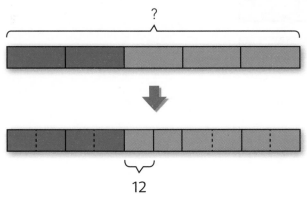

   1 unit = 12

   10 units = ☐

5. Of the beads in a box, $\frac{1}{4}$ are red.

   There are 24 more yellow beads than red beads.
   The remaining 76 beads are blue.
   How many beads are there altogether?

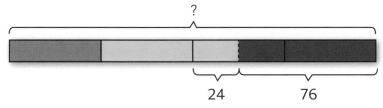

   $\frac{1}{2}$ ⟶ 24 + 76 = ☐ beads

   1 ⟶ ☐ beads

6.  Megan spent $\frac{2}{5}$ of her money on a doll and $\frac{1}{2}$ of the remainder on a musical box.
    She spent $8 more on the doll than on the musical box.
    How much money did she have left?

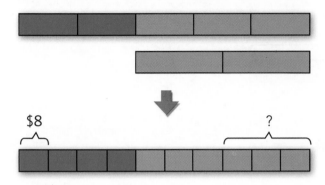

7.  10 jugs of water can fill $\frac{5}{8}$ of a bucket.

    Another 4 jugs and 5 cups of water are needed to fill the remaining part of the bucket.
    How many cups of water can the bucket hold?

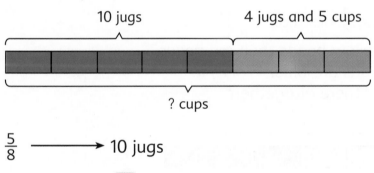

$\frac{5}{8}$ ⟶ 10 jugs

$\frac{1}{8}$ ⟶ ☐ jugs

$\frac{2}{8}$ ⟶ ☐ jugs

$\frac{1}{8}$ ⟶ ☐ cups

1 ⟶ ☐ cups

8. Mrs. Lee spends $\frac{3}{5}$ of her money on 3 bowls and 8 plates.

   With the rest of her money, she can buy another 6 bowls.
   If she spends all her money on plates only, how many plates can she buy?

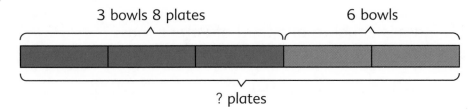

3 bowls 8 plates       6 bowls

? plates

9. Susan spent $\frac{1}{4}$ of her money on a book and $\frac{1}{2}$ of the remainder on a box of crayons.
   She spent $10 altogether.
   How much money did she have left?

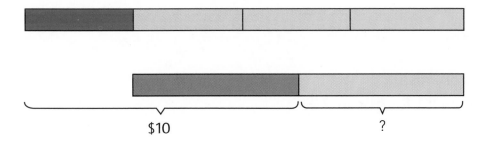

$10         ?

Exercise 13, pages 128–131

1. Mrs. Law bought $\frac{1}{2}$ of a cake. She cut it into 4 equal pieces. What fraction of the whole cake is each piece?

   (A) $\frac{1}{4}$        (B) $\frac{1}{2}$        (C) $\frac{2}{3}$        (D) $\frac{1}{8}$

2. Half of Jack's mass is equal to one third of Peter's mass. What is Jack's mass as a fraction of their total mass?

   (A) $\frac{5}{6}$        (B) $\frac{2}{3}$        (C) $\frac{2}{5}$        (D) $\frac{1}{5}$

3. Divide 15 by $2\frac{2}{5}$.

   (A) $6\frac{1}{4}$        (B) $\frac{4}{25}$        (C) 36        (D) $\frac{1}{36}$

4. The product of two numbers is $2\frac{1}{2}$. If one of the numbers is $1\frac{3}{7}$, which one of the following has the same value as the other number?

   (A) $\frac{7}{10} \div \frac{5}{2}$                     (B) $\frac{10}{7} \div \frac{5}{2}$

   (C) $\frac{5}{2} \div \frac{7}{10}$                     (C) $\frac{5}{2} \div \frac{10}{7}$

5. Select True or False.

   (a) There are 13 fourths in $3\frac{1}{4}$.                     True / False

   (b) There are 12 fourths in $\frac{3}{8}$.                     True / False

   (c) There are 7 fourths in $\frac{4}{7}$.                     True / False

6. Select True or False.

   (a) Natalie cuts a raffia $\frac{4}{5}$ m long into 8 pieces of equal length. Each piece is $\frac{2}{5}$ m.                     True / False

   (b) If $\frac{1}{4}$ kg of beef costs $6, then $\frac{2}{3}$ kg of beef costs $16.                     True / False

   (c) A rope is divided into two parts.

   One part is 300 cm long.

   This part is $\frac{2}{5}$ of the rope.

   The rope was 800 cm long.                     True / False

7. How many $\frac{2}{5}$'s are there in $\frac{5}{8}$?

8. Find the value of each of the following in its simplest form.
   (a) $\frac{2}{3} \times 45$
   (b) $\frac{35}{12} \times \frac{18}{7}$
   (c) $\frac{7}{9} \div 5$
   (d) $4 \div \frac{3}{8}$
   (e) $\frac{3}{5} \div \frac{5}{8}$
   (f) $\frac{14}{3} \times \frac{1}{7}$
   (g) $\frac{3}{4} \times \frac{8}{9}$
   (h) $\frac{5}{8} \times \frac{14}{15}$
   (i) $\frac{8}{12} \times \frac{16}{20}$
   (j) $\frac{3}{5} \div 3$
   (k) $\frac{7}{8} \div 2$
   (l) $\frac{4}{7} \div 12$
   (m) $\frac{5}{8} \times \frac{7}{10}$
   (n) $\frac{5}{8} \div 2$
   (o) $\frac{8}{5} \div \frac{4}{3}$
   (p) $\frac{4}{5} \div 3$
   (q) $\frac{7}{8} \div \frac{3}{2}$
   (r) $\frac{5}{6} \times 120$

9. Divide.
   (a) $8 \div \frac{1}{3}$
   (b) $\frac{4}{6} \div 10$
   (c) $\frac{5}{9} \div \frac{1}{3}$
   (d) $\frac{2}{7} \div \frac{4}{5}$
   (e) $8 \div \frac{2}{3}$
   (f) $\frac{3}{8} \div \frac{3}{7}$

10. Multiply or divide.
    (a) $4 \times \frac{3}{5}$
    (b) $\frac{5}{7} \times \frac{14}{15}$
    (c) $2\frac{4}{5} \times \frac{5}{11}$
    (d) $2\frac{2}{3} \times 5\frac{3}{4}$
    (e) $10 \div \frac{1}{6}$
    (f) $\frac{1}{5} \div 2$
    (g) $\frac{5}{8} \div 16$
    (h) $\frac{3}{4} \div 6$
    (i) $\frac{4}{5} \div \frac{1}{10}$
    (j) $\frac{5}{6} \div \frac{2}{3}$
    (k) $\frac{3}{8} \times \frac{2}{3}$
    (l) $3\frac{1}{5} \times 6\frac{1}{2}$
    (m) $4\frac{5}{6} \div 3$
    (n) $\frac{7}{8} \div \frac{3}{4}$

11. Of a bag of beans, $\frac{3}{4}$ weigh 4 kg. What is the mass of $\frac{1}{2}$ of the bag of beans in kilograms?

12. There are 1,500 workers in a factory. Of them, $\frac{5}{6}$ are men. Of the men, $\frac{3}{10}$ are single. How many single male workers are there in the factory?

13. Lauren spent $\frac{3}{5}$ of her money on a refrigerator. The refrigerator cost $756. How much money did she have left?

14. Mrs. Stewart made some pies. She sold $\frac{3}{5}$ of them and gave $\frac{1}{4}$ of the remainder to the food bank. If she had 150 pies left, how many pies did she sell?

15. Helen ate $\frac{1}{10}$ of a cake. She divided the remainder into 3 equal portions. What fraction of the cake was in each portion?

16. Of the 40 students in a class, $\frac{2}{5}$ are girls. Of the girls, $\frac{1}{4}$ wear glasses. How many girls do not wear glasses?

17. Jason had 14 boxes of apples for sale. There were 36 apples in each box. He sold $\frac{5}{6}$ of the apples and threw away $\frac{1}{6}$ of the remainder which were rotten. How many apples did he have left?

18. After spending $\frac{2}{5}$ of her money on a handbag and $20 on a belt, Mary had $25 left. How much money did she have at first?

19. Of a group of children, $\frac{3}{5}$ are boys. There are 12 more boys than girls. How many girls are there?

20. A concert started at 7:15 P.M. and lasted $1\frac{2}{3}$ hours. Of the people at the concert, $\frac{2}{5}$ are children. Of the children, $\frac{1}{4}$ are boys.
    (a)  At what time did the concert end?
    (b)  What fraction of the people at the concert are boys?

21. Of a sum of money, $\frac{5}{8}$ is $240. What is the value of the sum of money?

22. Sean spent $\frac{3}{5}$ of his money on a present for his mother.

He spent $\frac{3}{4}$ of the remainder on a present for his sister.
    (a)  What fraction of his money did he spend on the present for his sister?
    (b)  If he spent $450 altogether, how much money did he have left?

23. Andrew spent $\frac{1}{4}$ of his money on a book and $\frac{1}{2}$ of the remainder on a photo album. What fraction of his money did he spend altogether?

24. Mr. Ricci spent $\frac{1}{3}$ of his salary on food and $\frac{2}{5}$ of the remainder on transport.
    (a)  What fraction of his salary did he have left?
    (b)  If he had $600 left, find his salary.

25. Nicole bought 6 m of cloth to make a skirt and 3 shirts. She used $1\frac{3}{4}$ m for the skirt and $\frac{3}{4}$ m for each shirt. How much cloth did she have left?

26. David had 1,280 eggs. He sold $\frac{3}{5}$ of them on Saturday and $\frac{1}{4}$ of the remainder on Sunday. Find the total number of eggs sold on the two days.

27. Ryan withdrew $\frac{1}{4}$ of his savings from the bank. He spent $450 of it and had $150 left. How much money was his total savings in the bank at first?

28. Marisa spent $\frac{3}{4}$ of her money on a necklace. She spent $\frac{1}{2}$ of the remainder on some earrings. The necklace cost $30 more than the earrings. How much did the necklace cost?

29. Mrs. Mayne had $\frac{3}{5}$ kg of sugar. She used $\frac{1}{4}$ of it to make fruit pies. How much sugar did she use to make the fruit pies?

30. Henry bought 1 L of fruit juice. He kept $\frac{1}{4}$ L of it in a bottle and poured the remainder equally into 6 cups. How much fruit juice was there in each cup? Give the answer in liters.

31. A tank is $\frac{3}{5}$ filled with water. When 500 ml of water is poured out, the tank becomes $\frac{1}{2}$ full. Find the capacity of the tank in liters.

32. Of a box of paper clips, $\frac{2}{3}$ are red and the rest are green. If there are 120 red paper clips, how many green paper clips are there?

33. Mr. Reed packed $\frac{3}{4}$ kg of cookies equally into 3 bags. Find the mass of each bag of cookies. Give the answer in kilograms.

34. Mr. Lee's monthly salary is $2,500. He gives $\frac{1}{5}$ of it to his wife and spends $\frac{3}{4}$ of the remainder. How much money does he spend each month?

35. Emily used $\frac{3}{4}$ L of milk to fill 4 similar glasses. How many such glasses can 3 L of milk fill?

36. Mrs. Smith used $\frac{3}{8}$ of a bag of flour to bake cakes and $\frac{1}{5}$ of the remainder to bake biscuits. What fraction of the flour did she use altogether?

37. Mr. Venezia sold $\frac{1}{3}$ of his eggs in the morning and $\frac{1}{4}$ in the afternoon. He had 320 eggs left. How many eggs did he have at first?

38. Jerry made up the following word problem:

    John had rope that was $4\frac{4}{5}$ m long. He used $1\frac{3}{4}$ of it.

    How much rope did he use?

    Does this problem make sense? Why or why not?

Review 4, pages 132–136

# 5 PERIMETER AND AREA

## 1 Square Units

Find the area of each of these figures.

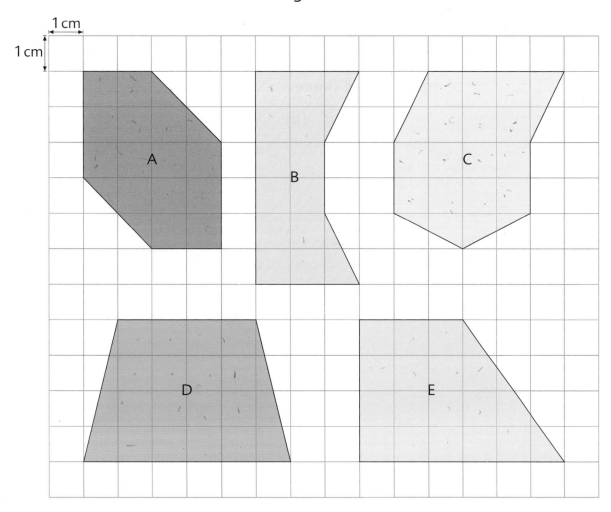

Which figure has the greatest area?
Which figure has the smallest area?
Which figures have the same area?

1.

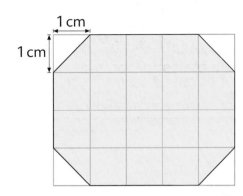

The area of the figure is  cm².

2. Find the area of each shaded figure.

(a)

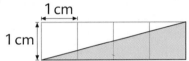

(b)

(c)

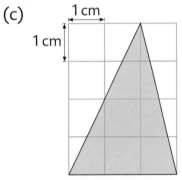

(d)

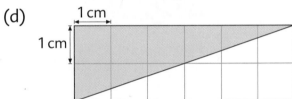

(e)

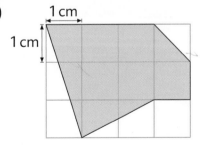

(f)

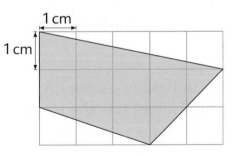

3. Find the area of each shaded triangle.

(a)

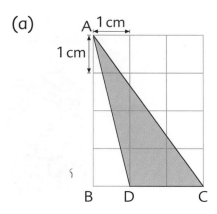

Area of Triangle ABC = 6 cm²

Area of Triangle ABD = 2 cm²

Area of Triangle ADC = 6 − 2

= [ ] cm²

(b)

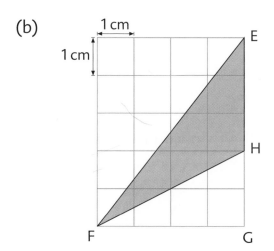

Area of Triangle EFG = [ ] cm²

Area of Triangle FGH = [ ] cm²

Area of Triangle EFH = [ ] cm²

(c)

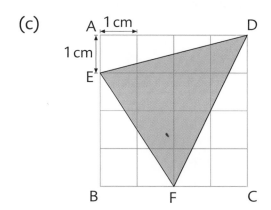

Area of Square ABCD = [ ] cm²

Area of Triangle AED = [ ] cm²

Area of Triangle EBF = [ ] cm²

Area of Triangle CDF = [ ] cm²

Area of Triangle DEF = [ ] cm²

Exercise 1, pages 137–138

4. Find the area of a rectangle measuring 6 cm by 3 cm.

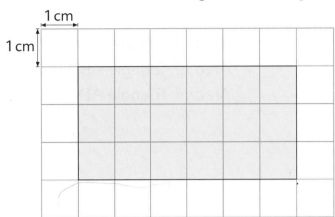

Area of a rectangle = length × width

Area = 6 cm × 3 cm

= ⬜ cm²

5. Find the area of each rectangle with the following measurements.
   (a) 12 cm by 5 cm
   (b) 14 cm by 21 cm
   (c) 6 m by 9 m

6. (a) A rectangle is made from 1 in. square tiles. What is its area?

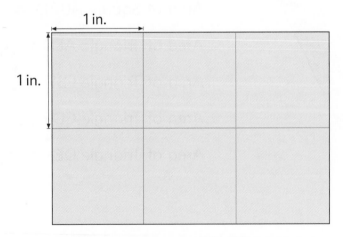

Area = 3 in. × 2 in.

= ⬜ in.²

(b) Another rectangle is made from the same number of $\frac{1}{4}$ in. square tiles. Find its area.

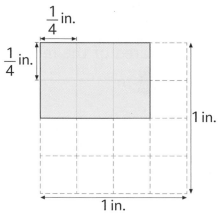

It would take 16 of the $\frac{1}{4}$ in.² tiles to cover an area of 1 in.². So the area of each tile $= \frac{1}{16}$ in².

$$\frac{1}{16} + \frac{1}{16} + \frac{1}{16} + \frac{1}{16} + \frac{1}{16} + \frac{1}{16} = 6 \times \frac{1}{16}$$
$$= \frac{6}{16} = \boxed{\phantom{xx}}$$

Length $= \frac{3}{4}$ in.　　　Width $= \frac{2}{4}$ in.

Area $=$ length $\times$ width
$$= \frac{3}{4} \times \frac{2}{4} = \boxed{\phantom{xx}}$$

The area is $\boxed{\phantom{xx}}$ in.²

(c) A rectangle is made from 6 rectangular tiles that are each $\frac{1}{4}$ in. by $\frac{1}{3}$ in.

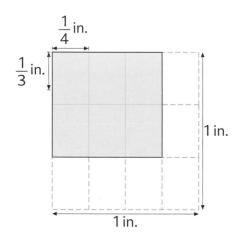

Will the final area be the same whether we have 2 rows of 3 or 1 row of 6?

What is the area of one single tile?
What is the area of the rectangle?

7. Find the area of a rectangle measuring 7 cm by $4\frac{3}{5}$ cm.

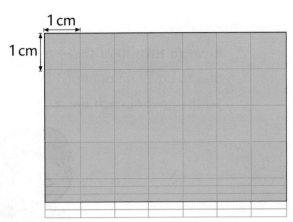

$7 \times 4\frac{3}{5} = $ 

The area of the rectangle is  m².

8. Find the area of a rectangle measuring $\frac{1}{3}$ m by $\frac{5}{6}$ m.

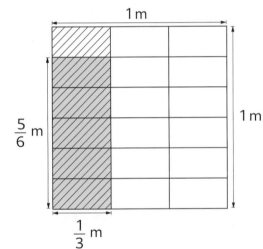

$\frac{1}{3} \times \frac{5}{6} = $ 

The area of the rectangle is  m².

9. Find the area of a rectangle measuring $2\frac{1}{4}$ ft by $7\frac{1}{2}$ ft.

$2\frac{1}{4} \times 7\frac{1}{2} = $ 

The area of the rectangle is  ft².

10. Find the area of a rectangle measuring $2\frac{5}{8}$ m by $3\frac{3}{5}$ m.

Exercise 2, pages 139–140

128

# ② Area of Composite Figures — Rectangles and Squares

Find the area of the shaded figure.

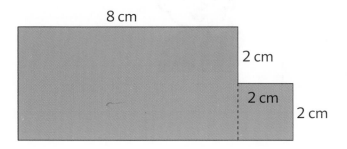

**Method 1:**

Find the total area of a rectangle and a square.

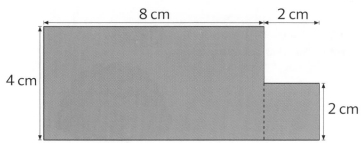

Area of rectangle = 8 × 4 = 32 cm$^2$

Area of square = 2 × 2 = 4 cm$^2$

Total area = 32 + 4 = [ ] cm$^2$

## Method 2:

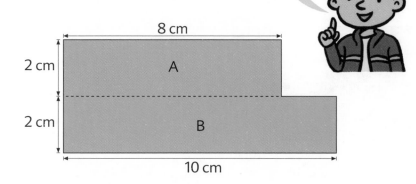

Find the total area of two rectangles.

Area of Rectangle A = 8 × 2 = 16 cm²

Area of Rectangle B = 10 × 2 = 20 cm²

Total area = 16 + 20 = ⬜ cm²

## Method 3:

Subtract the area of a square from the area of a rectangle.

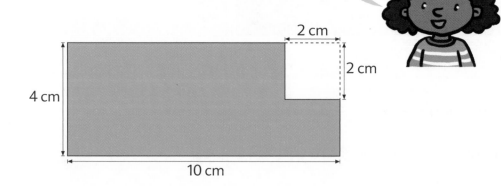

Area of rectangle = 10 × 4 = 40 cm²

Area of square = 2 × 2 = 4 cm²

Area of the shaded figure = 40 − 4 = ⬜ cm²

1. In each figure, draw a straight line to divide the figure into two parts of equal area.

(a)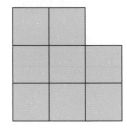

(b)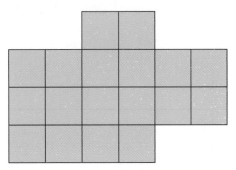

2. Find the area and perimeter of each figure.
   (All the lines meet at right angles.)

(a)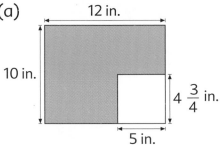

6 cm   6 cm

$4\frac{1}{2}$ cm

8 cm

6 cm

15 cm

(b)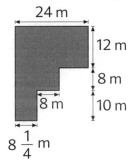

24 m

12 m

8 m

8 m   10 m

$8\frac{1}{4}$ m

3. Find the shaded area of each rectangle.

(a)

12 in.

10 in.

$4\frac{3}{4}$ in.

5 in.

(b)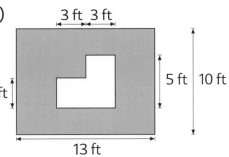

3 ft  3 ft

3 ft

5 ft   10 ft

13 ft

4. Find the shaded area of the rectangle.

2 m

3 m

2 m

3 m

5 m   2 m     7 m

131

Exercise 3, page 141

# 3 Area of a Triangle

Find the area of each shaded triangle and its related rectangle.

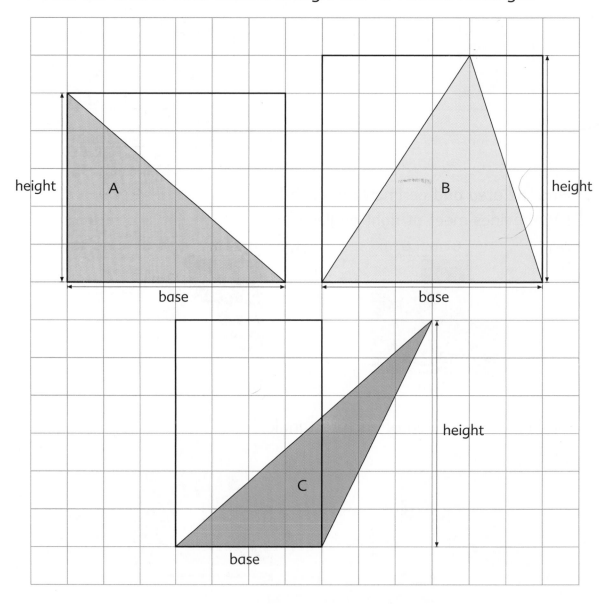

Compare the area of each triangle with the area of its related rectangle.

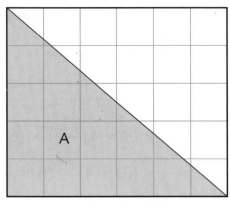

Area of related rectangle
= 6 × 5
= 30 square units

Area of Triangle A

=  square units

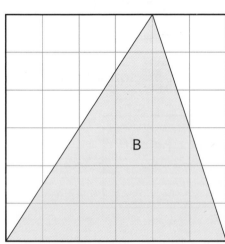
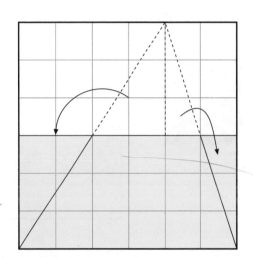

Area of related rectangle = 6 × 6
= 36 square units

Area of Triangle B =  square units

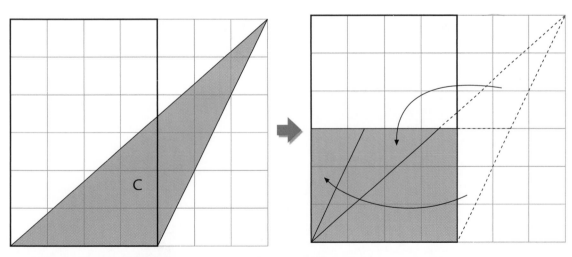

Area of related rectangle = 4 × 6
= 24 square units

Area of Triangle C =  square units

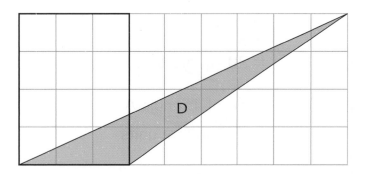

Area of related rectangle
= 3 × 4
= 12 square units

Area of Triangle D

$= \frac{1}{2} \times (9 \times 4) - \frac{1}{2} \times (6 \times 4)$

$= \frac{1}{2} \times [(9 \times 4) - (6 \times 4)]$

$= \frac{1}{2} \times (9 - 6) \times 4$

$= \frac{1}{2} \times 3 \times 4$

= ⬚ square units

Area of triangle $= \frac{1}{2} \times$ Area of related rectangle

Area of triangle $= \frac{1}{2} \times$ base × height

$A = \frac{1}{2} \times b \times h$

1.  For each shaded triangle, name the height which is related to the given base of the triangle.

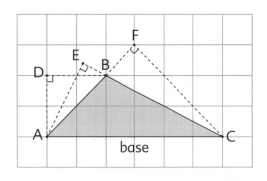

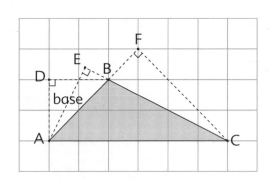

134

2. Find the area of each triangle.

(a)

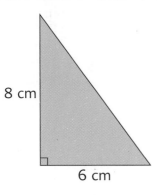

8 cm

6 cm

Area of the triangle

$= \frac{1}{2} \times 6 \times 8$

$=$ ⬜ cm²

(b)

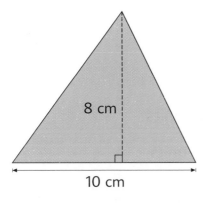

8 cm

10 cm

Area of the triangle

$= \frac{1}{2} \times 10 \times 8$

$=$ ⬜ cm²

(c)

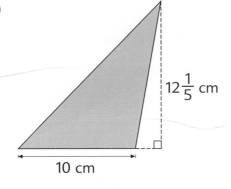

$12\frac{1}{5}$ cm

10 cm

Area of the triangle

$= \frac{1}{2} \times 10 \times 12\frac{1}{5}$

$=$ ⬜ cm²

Exercise 4, pages 142–145

3.

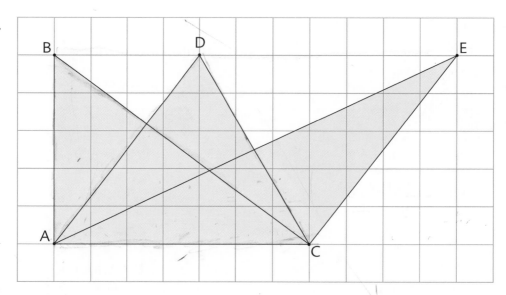

(a) Area of Triangle ABC = ☐ square units

(b) Area of Triangle ADC = ☐ square units

(c) Area of Triangle AEC = ☐ square units

4. Find the area of each shaded triangle.

(a)

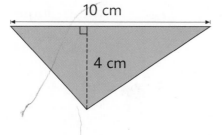

10 cm

4 cm

(b)

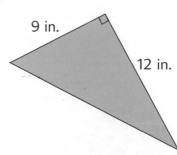

9 in.

12 in.

(c)

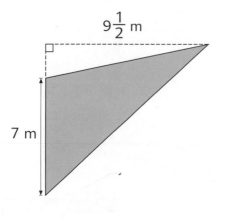

$9\frac{1}{2}$ m

7 m

(d)

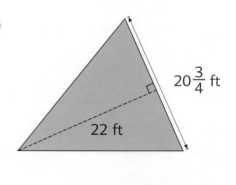

$20\frac{3}{4}$ ft

22 ft

Exercise 5, pages 146–148

5. Find the area of each shaded triangle.

(a)

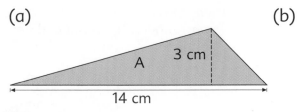

(b)

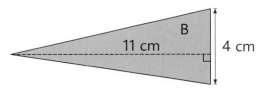

(c)

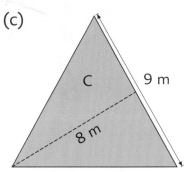

(d)

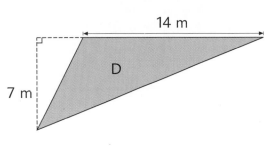

6. Find the area of each shaded triangle.

(a)

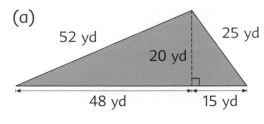

(b)

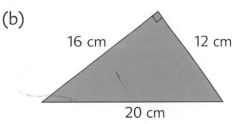

(c)

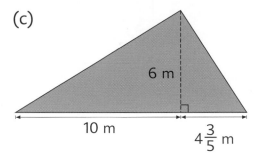

(d)

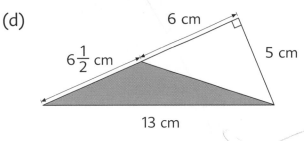

7. Find the shaded area of each rectangle.

(a)

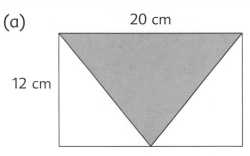

(b)

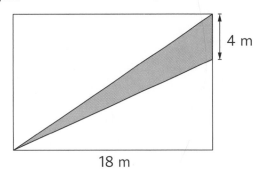

8. Find the shaded area of each rectangle.

(a)

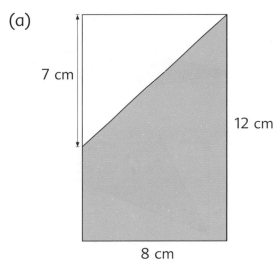

7 cm

12 cm

8 cm

In each figure, the unshaded part is a triangle.

Find the area of the triangle first.

(b)

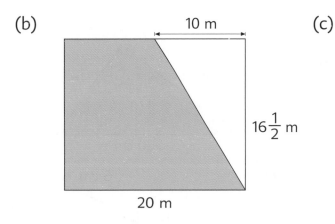

10 m

$16\frac{1}{2}$ m

20 m

(c)

14 cm

20 cm

8 cm

9. Find the area of each shaded figure.

(a)

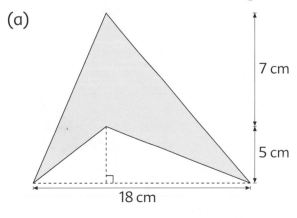

7 cm

5 cm

18 cm

(b)

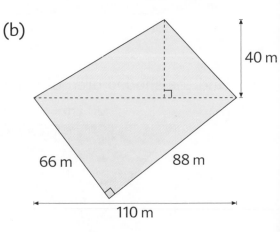

40 m

66 m

88 m

110 m

Exercise 6, pages 149–151

# 4 Area of a Parallelogram

Find the area of the parallelogram.

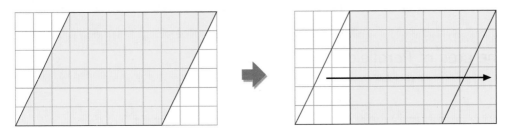

Compare the area of the parallelogram with the area of its related rectangle.

Area of rectangle = 8 × 6

= ▢ square units

Area of parallelogram = ▢ square units

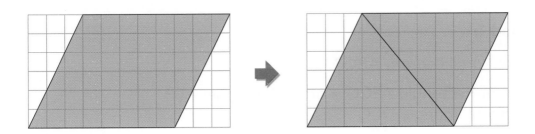

Divide the parallelogram into two equal triangles.
Compare the area of the parallelogram with the area of the two triangles.

Area of one triangle = $\frac{1}{2}$ × 8 × 6

= ▢ square units

Area of both triangles = 2 × $\frac{1}{2}$ × 8 × 6

= 8 × 6

= ▢ square units

Area of parallelogram = ▢ square units

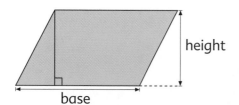

height

base

Area of parallelogram = base × height
$$A = b \times h$$

1. Find the area of Parallelogram ABCD.

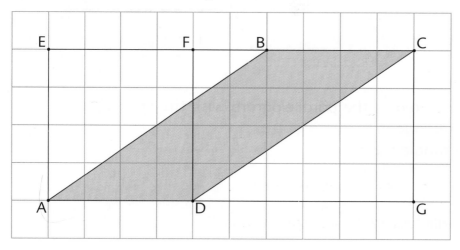

## Method 1:

Area of Parallelogram ABCD

= Area of Rectangle AECG − area of Triangle AEB
  − area of Triangle DCG

$= 10 \times 4 - \frac{1}{2} \times (6 \times 4) - \frac{1}{2} \times (6 \times 4)$

$= 10 \times 4 - 6 \times 4$

$= (10 - 6) \times 4$

$= 4 \times 4$

= ☐ square units

## Method 2:

Area of Parallelogram ABCD

= base × height

= 4 × ☐

= ☐ square units

2. Find the area of each parallelogram.

(a)

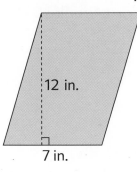

12 in.

7 in.

Area of the parallelogram
= 7 × 12

=  in.²

(b)

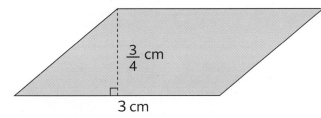

$\frac{3}{4}$ cm

3 cm

Area of the parallelogram

= $3 \times \frac{3}{4}$

= ⬛ cm²

(c)

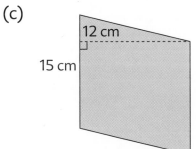

12 cm

15 cm

Area of the parallelogram

= ⬛ cm²

(d)

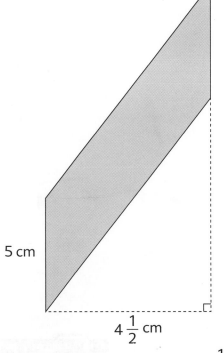

5 cm

$4\frac{1}{2}$ cm

Area of the parallelogram

= ⬛ cm²

3. Find the area of each shaded figure.
   Each figure is made from parallelograms and/or triangles.

   (a)

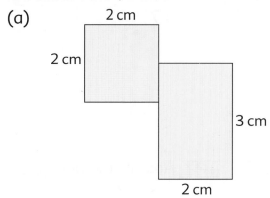

2 cm

2 cm

3 cm

2 cm

   (b)

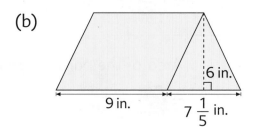

6 in.

9 in.

$7\frac{1}{5}$ in.

   (c)

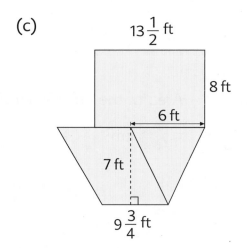

$13\frac{1}{2}$ ft

8 ft

6 ft

7 ft

$9\frac{3}{4}$ ft

   (d)

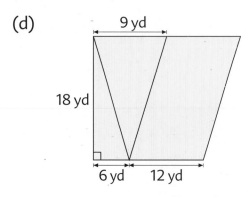

9 yd

18 yd

6 yd    12 yd

Exercise 7, pages 152–153

# REVIEW 5

1. A square has a side of 6 cm. What is the width of a rectangle with the same area as the square and a length of 9 cm?
   (A) 3 cm      (B) 4 cm      (C) 5 cm      (D) 6 cm

2. The figure is made up of two squares of sides 8 cm and 9 cm.

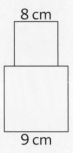

8 cm

9 cm

   (a) What is the perimeter of the figure?
   (A) 51 cm      (B) 52 cm      (C) 63 cm      (D) 68 cm

   (b) What is the area of the figure?
   (A) 389 cm²      (B) 145 cm²      (C) 68 cm²      (D) 52 cm²

3. The figure is made up of 4 squares. If the area of each square is 49 cm², find the perimeter of the figure.

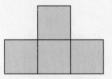

   (A) 28 cm      (B) 28 cm²      (C) 70 cm      (D) 91 cm

4. Select True or False.
   (a) The area of a triangle $= \frac{1}{2} \times$ length $\times$ width      True / False

   (b) The area of a parallelogram $=$ length $\times$ width      True / False

5. Select True or False.
   (a) The area of a square made up of 4 smaller squares each with sides 3 cm is 6 cm².      True / False

   (b) The area of a square made up of 9 tiles each with a side of half a square centimeter is $4\frac{1}{2}$ cm².      True / False

6. Find the area and the perimeter of the shaded figure.

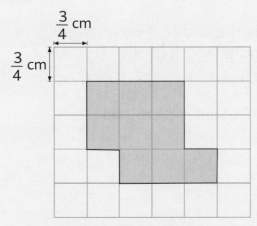

7. Find the perimeter and area of each figure.
(All the lines meet at right angles.)

(a)

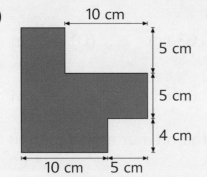

10 cm
5 cm
5 cm
4 cm
10 cm    5 cm

(b)

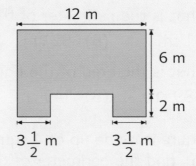

12 m
6 m
2 m
$3\frac{1}{2}$ m    $3\frac{1}{2}$ m

(c)

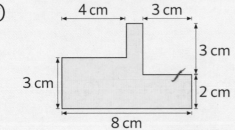

4 cm    3 cm
3 cm
3 cm
2 cm
8 cm

(d)

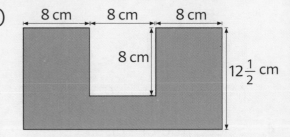

8 cm    8 cm    8 cm
8 cm
$12\frac{1}{2}$ cm

(e)

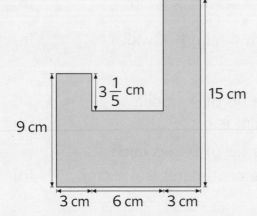

$3\frac{1}{5}$ cm
15 cm
9 cm
3 cm    6 cm    3 cm

8. A picture measuring 28 cm by 25 cm is mounted on rectangular cardboard, leaving a margin of 5 cm all around. Find the area of the cardboard not covered by the picture.

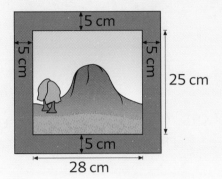

9. A room is 6 m long and 5 m wide. Of it, $\frac{2}{3}$ is covered by a carpet.
   (a) Find the area of the carpet.
   (b) Find the cost of the carpet if 1 m² of it costs $80.

10. Connie is training for a $4\frac{4}{5}$ km run on a rectangular running track. If the track measures 50 m wide and has an area of 7,500 m², how many rounds must she run?

11. (a) The bedroom in a house is 7 ft by $8\frac{1}{2}$ ft. What is the area of the bedroom?
    (b) The entire house has an area about 8 times that of the bedroom. What is the square footage of the house?

12. What is the area of each triangle?
    (a)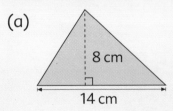

    (b)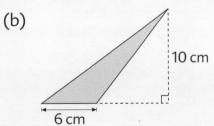

13. Find the area of each shaded triangle.
    (a)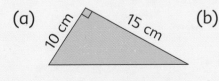
    (b)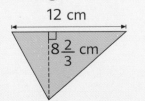
    (c)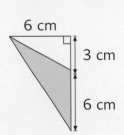

14. The perimeter of the triangle is 36 m. Find its area.

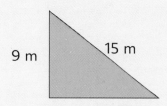

9 m    15 m

15. The perimeter of the shaded triangle is 60 cm. Find its area.

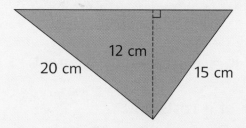

20 cm    12 cm    15 cm

16. Find the area of each shaded part.

(a)

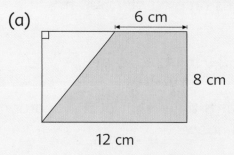

6 cm
8 cm
12 cm

(b)

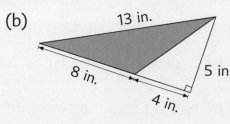

13 in.
8 in.
4 in.
5 in.

(c)

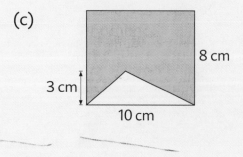

8 cm
3 cm
10 cm

(d)

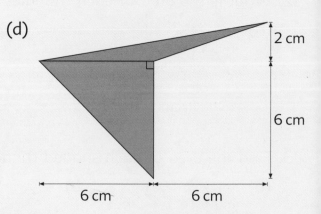

2 cm
6 cm
6 cm    6 cm

17. Find the shaded area of each rectangle.

(a)

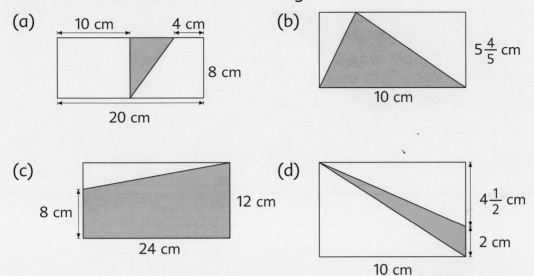

10 cm   4 cm

8 cm

20 cm

(b)

$5\frac{4}{5}$ cm

10 cm

(c)

8 cm

24 cm

12 cm

(d)

$4\frac{1}{2}$ cm

2 cm

10 cm

18. This figure is made up of 8 triangles.
The base of each triangle is 6 cm and the height is 6 cm.
What is the area of the figure?

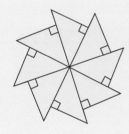

19. The figure is made up of a square and a triangle.
If the area of the square is 64 cm², find the area of the triangle.

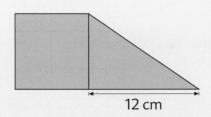

12 cm

20. Find the area of the shaded part of the rectangle.

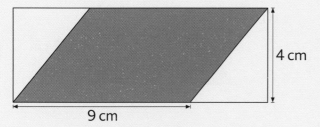

4 cm

9 cm

21. Find the area of the parallelogram.

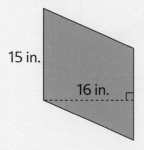

15 in.

16 in.

22. The figure is made up of a parallelogram and a triangle.
Find its area.

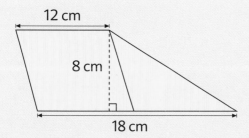

12 cm

8 cm

18 cm

23. The area of a parallelogram is 53 cm². 
If the height is 6 cm, what is the length of the base?

24. Joy says that the area of the triangle is equal to half
the area of the rectangle shown.
Is she correct? Explain why or why not.

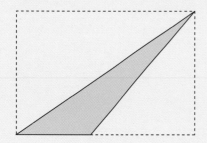

Review 5, pages 154—160

# 6 RATIO

## 1 Finding Ratio

David and John visited an art supply store. David bought 3 bottles of blue ink and 2 bottles of red ink.

The **ratio** of the number of bottles of blue ink to the number of bottles of red ink is 3 : 2.

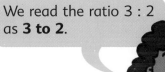

We read the ratio 3 : 2 as **3 to 2**.

John bought 5 boxes of blue pens and 2 boxes of red pens.

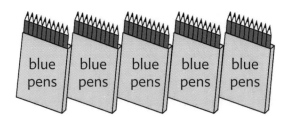   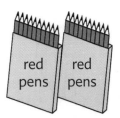

5 boxes to 2 boxes.

The **ratio** of the number of blue pens to the number of red pens is 5 : 2.

149

1.  Ricardo mixed 3 cans of red paint with 1 can of white paint.

The ratio of the number of cans of red paint to the number of cans of white paint is 3 : 1.

The ratio of the number of cans of white paint to the number of cans of red paint is ☐ : ☐.

2.

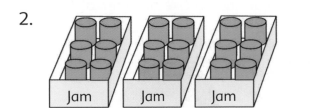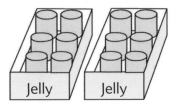

The ratio of the number of jars of jam to the number of jars of jelly is 3 : 2.

The ratio of the number of jars of jelly to the number of jars of jam is ☐ : ☐.

3.

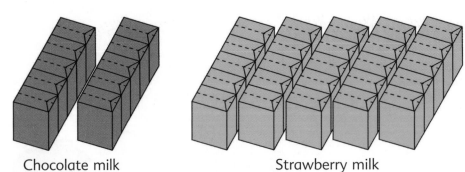

Chocolate milk                    Strawberry milk

The ratio of the number of packets of chocolate milk to the number of packets of strawberry milk is ☐ : ☐.

The ratio of the number of packets of strawberry milk to the number of packets of chocolate milk is ☐ : ☐.

4.

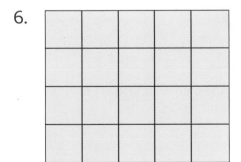

1 unit

3 units to 2 units.

The ratio of the number of buckets to the number of shovels is ▢ : ▢.

5.

1 unit

P ▢

Q ▢

3 units to 7 units.

The ratio of the length of P to the length of Q is ▢ : ▢.

6.

The ratio of the length of the rectangle to its width is ▢ : ▢.

7.

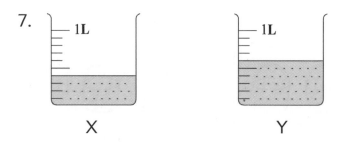

X                          Y

The ratio of the volume of sand in Container X to the volume of sand in Container Y is ⬜ : ⬜.

8.

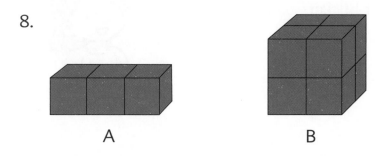

A                          B

The ratio of the number of cubes in Solid A to the number of cubes in Solid B is ⬜ : ⬜.

9.

C                          D

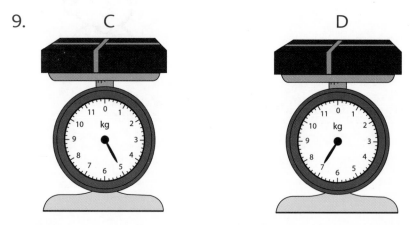

The ratio of the mass of Package C to the mass of Package D is ⬜ : ⬜.

Exercise 1, pages 161–162

## ② Equivalent Ratios

John has 8 quarters and Peter has 12 quarters.

John

Peter

The ratio of John's money to Peter's money is 8 : 12.

Now, John and Peter put their quarters into groups of 2.

John

4 units to 6 units.

Peter

The ratio of John's money to Peter's money is 4 : 6.

Now, John and Peter put their quarters into groups of 4.

John

2 units to 3 units.

Peter

The ratio of John's money to Peter's money is 2 : 3.

8 : 12, 4 : 6 and 2 : 3 are **equivalent ratios**.
2 : 3 is a ratio in its simplest form.

1. Express each ratio in its simplest form.
   (a)  4 : 10
        4 : 10 = ▢ : ▢

   2 is a common factor
   of 4 and 10.
   Divide 4 and 10 by 2.

   $\cancel{4} : \cancel{10}$
   2      5

   (b)  12 : 18
        12 : 18 = ▢ : ▢

   6 is a common factor
   of 12 and 18.
   Divide 12 and 18 by 6.

   $\cancel{12} : \cancel{18}$
   2      3

2. Express each ratio in its simplest form.
   (a)  8 : 10              (b)  10 : 6
   (c)  6 : 24              (d)  21 : 14

3. There are 15 ducks and 12 chickens in a farm.
   Find the ratio of the number of ducks to the number of chickens.

   15 : 12 = ▢ : ▢

   Write the ratio 15 : 12
   in its simplest form.

   The ratio of the number of ducks to the number of chickens

   is ▢ : ▢.

Exercise 2, pages 163—164

4. There are 40 students in a class. Of them, 25 are boys.
   Find the ratio of the number of boys to the number of girls in the class.

   Number of girls = 40 − 25 = 15

   Number of boys = 25

Write the ratio 25 : 15 in its simplest form.

   25 : 15 = ▢ : ▢

   The ratio of the number of boys to the number of girls is ▢ : ▢.

5. The ratio of the length of Ribbon A to the length of Ribbon B is 7 : 4.
   If Ribbon A is 21 m long, find the length of Ribbon B.

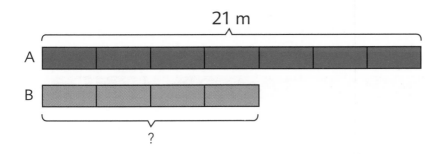

7 : 4 means 7 units to 4 units.

   7 units = 21 m

   1 unit = ▢ m

   4 units = ▢ m

   The length of Ribbon B is ▢ m.

6. Lucy and Mary shared $35 in the ratio 4 : 3.
   How much money did Lucy receive?

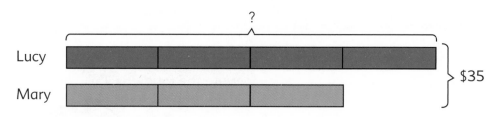

7 units = $35

1 units = $◻

4 units = $◻

Lucy received $◻.

7. The ratio of the mass of Package X to the mass of Package Y
   is 5 : 3. If the mass of Package X is 40 kg, find the total mass
   of the two packages.

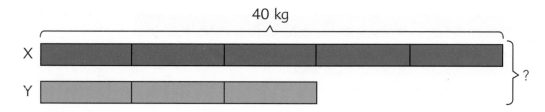

5 units = 40 kg

1 unit = ◻ kg

8 units = ◻ kg

The total mass is ◻ kg.

Exercise 3, pages 165–167

# ③ Combining Three Quantities

There are 12 triangles, 6 squares, and 4 circles.

(a) Find the ratio of the number of triangles to the number of squares.

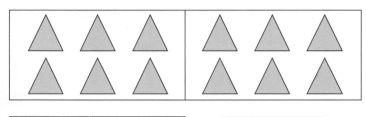

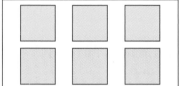

2 units to 1 unit.

The ratio of the number of triangles to the number

of squares is ▢ : ▢ .

(b) Find the ratio of the number of triangles to the number of squares to the number of circles.

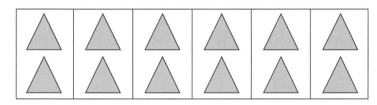

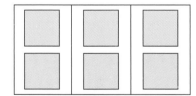

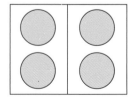

6 units to 3 units to 2 units.

The ratio of the number of triangles to the number

of squares to the number of circles is ▢ : ▢ : ▢ .

1. Write each ratio in its simplest form.

   (a) 12 : 6 : 4

   12 : 6 : 4 = ☐ : ☐ : ☐

   2 is a common factor of 12, 6, and 4.
   Divide 12, 6, and 4 by 2.

   $$\frac{12}{6} : \frac{6}{3} : \frac{4}{2}$$

   (b) 20 : 10 : 15

   20 : 10 : 15 = ☐ : ☐ : ☐

   5 is a common factor of 20, 10, and 15.
   Divide 20, 10, and 15 by 5.

   $$\frac{20}{4} : \frac{10}{2} : \frac{15}{3}$$

2. In a fruit orchard, there are 60 peach trees, 20 plum trees, and 35 apricot trees. What is the ratio of the number of peach trees to the number of plum trees to the number of apricot trees in its simplest form?

   60 : 20 : 35 =  :  :

   The ratio of the number of peach trees to the number of plum trees

   to the number of apricot trees is ☐ : ☐ : ☐ .

Exercise 4, pages 168–169

3. 20 L of water are poured into 3 buckets A, B, and C in the ratio 2 : 3 : 5. Find the volume of water in Bucket C.

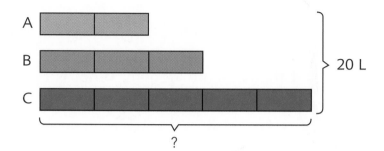

10 units = 20 L

1 unit =  L

5 units =  L

The volume of water in Bucket C is  liters.

4. A pole, 90 cm long, is painted red, yellow, and blue in the ratio 3 : 5 : 2.

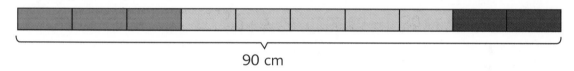

90 cm

(a) What length of the pole is painted red?
10 units = 90 cm

1 unit =  cm

3 units =  cm

The length of the pole painted red is  cm.

(b) What length of the pole is painted blue?

2 units is $\frac{1}{5}$ of 10 units.

$\frac{1}{5}$ x 90 cm =  cm

The length of the pole painted blue is  cm.

Exercise 5, pages 170—171

1. 2 : 5 is the same as _____.
   (A) 3 : 5      (B) 4 : 10      (C) 5 : 12      (D) 6 : 8

2. There are 48 adults in a shop. Of them 30 are women. What is the ratio of the number of men to the number of women?
   (A) 3 : 5      (B) 5 : 3      (C) 5 : 8      (D) 8 : 5

3. A sum of $108 was shared among Alice, Mary, and Linda in the ratio 5 : 4 : 3 respectively. Mary received _____.
   (A) $27      (B) $36      (C) $45      (D) $81

4. Rectangle A is 8 cm long and 4 cm wide. Rectangle B is 4 cm long and 2 cm wide. The ratio of the area of Rectangle A to Rectangle B is _____.
   (A) 2 : 1      (B) 4 : 1      (C) 1 : 2      (D) 1 : 4

5. Select True or False.
   (a) The ratio 3 : 5 also means 3 + 5.      True / False
   (b) The ratio 2 : 7 is the same as 7 : 2.      True / False

6. Select True or False.
   (a) John is 12. Peter is 4 years older than John.
   The ratio of Peter's age to John's age is 4 : 3.      True / False
   (b) There are 7 nickels and 14 dimes.
   The ratio of nickels to the total number of coins
   is 1 : 4.      True / False

7. Express each ratio in its simplest form.
   (a) 2 : 10      (b) 6 : 12      (c) 21 : 14
   (d) 20 : 5      (e) 40 : 16      (f) 4 : 100

8. Find the missing number in each ▢.
   (a) 5 : 6 = ▢ : 18      (b) 30 : 48 = 5 : ▢

9. Express 20 : 12 : 56 in its simplest form.

10. There are 36 mugs in a box. Of them 8 are blue and the rest are red. What is the ratio of the number of red mugs to the number of blue mugs? Write the answer in its simplest form.

11. The ratio of the number of female members to the number of male members in a club is 3 : 5. If there are 48 female members, how many members are there altogether?

12. John and Peter share $180 in the ratio 3 : 2. How much more money does John receive than Peter?

13. The ratio of the length of a rectangular field to its width is 4 : 3. The length of the field is 20 m. Find its area and perimeter.

14. David cuts a rope 60 m long into two pieces in the ratio 2 : 3. What is the length of the shorter piece of rope?

15. The ratio of Adam's mass to John's mass is 6 : 5. If Adam has a mass of 48 kg, find John's mass.

16. The ratio of the number of men to the number of women in a club is 5 : 7. There are 12 more women than men. How many members are there altogether?

17. The ratio of the number of boys to the number of girls is 2 : 5. If there are 100 boys, how many children are there altogether?

18. Sean, Ryan, and John shared a sum of money in the ratio 3 : 4 : 5. If Sean received $30, what was the sum of money shared?

19. Lily, Carla, and Gwen shared $156 in the ratio 3 : 2 : 7.
    (a) How much money did Carla receive?
    (b) How much more money did Gwen receive than Lily?

20. Matt had some quarters and dimes. The ratio of the value of the quarters to the value of the dimes is 25 : 12. What is the ratio of the number of quarters to the number of dimes? Explain how you found the answer.

Review 6, pages 172–176

# GLOSSARY

| Word | Meaning |
|---|---|
| **approximation** | The **approximation** of a number is the number obtained after we have rounded it to the nearest thousands, millions or billions.<br><br>2,546 rounded to the nearest thousand is 3,000.<br>2,546 is **approximately** 3,000. |
| **billion** | One **billion** is one thousand millions, or 1,000,000,000. |
| **composite number** | A **composite number** has factors other than 1 and itself.<br><br>6 is a composite number because its factors are 2 and 3 apart from 1 and itself. |
| **equivalent ratios** | **Equivalent ratios** are two or more ratios that have the same value.<br><br>1 : 2, 2 : 4, and 4 : 8 are **equivalent ratios**. |
| **exponent** | The **exponent** tells us how many times to multiply the base with itself.<br><br>$$4^3 = 4 \times 4 \times 4$$<br><br>base    **exponent** |

| Word | Meaning |
| --- | --- |
| **factor** | A **factor** is an exact divisor of a number.<br><br>4 is a **factor** of 16 since 16 is exactly divisible by 4. |
| **greatest common factor** | **Greatest common factor** is the common factor of two numbers that has the greatest value.<br><br>Factors of 18: **1**, **2**, **3**, **6**, 9, 18<br>Factors of 24: **1**, **2**, **3**, 4, **6**, 8, 12, 24<br><br>1, 2, 3 and 6 are common factors of 18 and 24.<br>6 is the **greatest common factor** of 18 and 24. |
| **improper fraction** | An **improper fraction** has a value equal to, or greater than one. The numerator is equal to or greater than the denominator.<br><br>$\frac{7}{4}$, $\frac{9}{7}$, and $\frac{4}{3}$ are improper fractions. |
| **like fractions** | **Like fractions** are two or more fractions with common denominators.<br><br>$\frac{4}{7}$ and $\frac{6}{7}$ are like fractions. |

| Word | Meaning |
|---|---|
| **lowest common multiple** | **Lowest common multiple** is the smallest number that is a common multiple of two numbers.<br><br>Multiples of 2: 2, **4**, 6, **8**, 10, **12** ...<br>Multiples of 4: **4**, **8**, **12** ...<br><br>4, 8, and 12 are common multiples of 2 and 4.<br>4 is the **lowest common multiple** of 2 and 4. |
| **mixed number** | A **mixed number** is made up of a whole number and a fraction.<br><br>$1\frac{6}{7}$, $4\frac{8}{9}$, and $3\frac{2}{5}$ are mixed numbers. |
| **multiple** | A **multiple** is the product of two factors of a number.<br><br>20 is a **multiple** of 2 since $2 \times 10 = 20$. |
| **order of operations** | The order in which we solve an expression containing two or more operation signs. Using the **order of operations**, multiplication and division is done first from left to right, followed by addition or subtraction from left to right. |

| Word | Meaning |
|---|---|
| **period** | Starting from the right, each group of 3 digits in a number forms a **period**. Each **period** is separated by a comma.<br><br>In the number 7,465,243,082, '082' forms a **period**, '243' forms another **period** and so on. |
| **prime factor** | A **prime factor** is any factor of a number that is a prime number.<br><br>The factors of 10 are 1, 2, 5 and 10. The **prime factors** of 10 are 2 and 5. |
| **prime factorization** | **Prime factorization** is the process of factoring a composite number into its prime factors. |
| **prime number** | A number is a prime number if:<br>(a) it is greater than one, and<br>(b) it has only and exactly two factors: 1 and itself.<br><br>Example:<br>5 is a prime number because it is greater than 1, and its only two factors are 1 and 5 (itself). |

| Word | Meaning |
|------|---------|
| **ratio** | **Ratio** is the comparison of two quantities expressed in the form x : y.<br><br>Tom buys 5 pencils and 9 pens. The ratio of the number of pencils to the number of pens Tom buys is 5 : 9. |

# Grade 5 Curriculum Map

| Common Core State Standards | | Unit | Student Textbook Lessons | Student Workbook Exercises |
|---|---|---|---|---|
| **OPERATIONS & ALGEBRAIC THINKING** | | | | |
| **Write and interpret numerical expressions.** | | | | |
| 5.OA.1 | Use parentheses, brackets, or braces in numerical expressions, and evaluate expressions with these symbols. | **Unit 2 Lesson 1 Order of Operations** | **TB 5A:** 30–32 | **WB 5A:** 30–32 |
| 5.OA.2 | Write simple expressions that record calculations with numbers, and interpret numerical expressions without evaluating them. *For example, express the calculation "add 8 and 7, then multiply by 2" as 2 × (8 + 7). Recognize that 3 × (18932 + 921) is three times as large as 18932 + 921, without having to calculate the indicated sum or product.* | **Unit 2 Lesson 1 Order of Operations** | **TB 5A:** 33–34 | **WB 5A:** 33–34 |
| **Analyze patterns and relationships.** | | | | |
| 5.OA.3 | Generate two numerical patterns using two given rules. Identify apparent relationships between corresponding terms. Form ordered pairs consisting of corresponding terms from the two patterns, and graph the ordered pairs on a coordinate plane. *For example, given the rule "Add 3" and the starting number 0, and given the rule "Add 6" and the starting number 0, generate terms in the resulting sequences, and observe that the terms in one sequence are twice the corresponding terms in the other sequence. Explain informally why this is so.* | **Unit 10 Lesson 4 Line Graphs** | **TB 5B:** 97–101 | **WB 5B:** 79–83 |
| **NUMBER & OPERATIONS IN BASE TEN** | | | | |
| **Understand the place value system.** | | | | |
| 5.NBT.1 | Recognize that in a multi-digit number, a digit in one place represents 10 times as much as it represents in the place to its right and $\frac{1}{10}$ of what it represents in the place to its left. | **Unit 1 Lesson 1 Large Numbers** **Unit 1 Lesson 5 Multiplying by Tens, Hundreds or Thousands** | **TB 5A:** 8–9, 22, 24 | **WB 5A:** 5–7, 18–20, 21–24 |

| Common Core State Standards | | Unit | Student Textbook Lessons | Student Workbook Exercises |
|---|---|---|---|---|
| | | **Unit 1 Lesson 6 Dividing by Tens, Hundreds or Thousands** | | |
| 5.NBT.2 | Explain patterns in the number of zeros of the product when multiplying a number by powers of 10, and explain patterns in the placement of the decimal point when a decimal is multiplied or divided by a power of 10. Use whole-number exponents to denote powers of 10. | **Unit 1 Lesson 5 Multiplying by Tens, Hundreds or Thousands**  **Unit 7 Lesson 5 Multiplication by Tens, Hundreds, or Thousands**  **Unit 7 Lesson 6 Division by Tens, Hundreds, or Thousands** | **TB 5A:** 22–23  **TB 5B:** 28–35 | **WB 5A:** 18–20  **WB 5B:** 46–48 |
| 5.NBT.3a | Read, write, and compare decimals to thousandths. Read and write decimals to thousandths using base-ten numerals, number names, and expanded form, e.g., $347.392 = 3 \times 100 + 4 \times 10 + 7 \times 1 + 3 \times \left(\frac{1}{10}\right) + 9 \times \left(\frac{1}{100}\right) + 2 \times \left(\frac{1}{1000}\right)$. | **Unit 7 Lesson 1 Tenths, Hundredths and Thousandths** | **TB 5B:** 8–11 | **WB 5B:** 5–6 |
| 5.NBT.3b | Read, write, and compare decimals to thousandths. Compare two decimals to thousandths based on meanings of the digits in each place, using >, =, and < symbols to record the results of comparisons. | **Unit 7 Lesson 1 Tenths, Hundredths and Thousandths** | **TB 5B:** 12 | **WB 5B:** 7 |

| Common Core State Standards | | Unit | Student Textbook Lessons | Student Workbook Exercises |
|---|---|---|---|---|
| 5.NBT.4 | Use place value understanding to round decimals to any place. | **Unit 7 Lesson 2 Approximation** **Unit 7 Lesson 3 Add and Subtract Decimals** **Unit 7 Lesson 4 Multiply and Divide Decimals by a 1-Digit Whole Number** | **TB 5B:** 14–16, 18, 21, 24–25 | **WB 5B:** 8–9, 12–14 |
| **Perform operations with multi-digit whole numbers and with decimals to hundredths.** | | | | |
| 5.NBT.5 | Fluently multiply multi-digit whole numbers using the standard algorithm. | **Unit 2 Lesson 4 Multiplication by a 2-Digit Whole Number** | **TB 5A:** 44–46 | **WB 5A:** **48–50** |
| 5.NBT.6 | Find whole-number quotients of whole numbers with up to four-digit dividends and two-digit divisors, using strategies based on place value, the properties of operations, and/or the relationship between multiplication and division. Illustrate and explain the calculation by using equations, rectangular arrays, and/or area models. | **Unit 2 Lesson 5 Division by a 2-Digit Whole Number** | **TB 5A:** 47–53 | **WB 5A:** 51–55 |
| 5.NBT.7 | Add, subtract, multiply, and divide decimals to hundredths, using concrete models or drawings and strategies based on place value, properties of operations, and/or the relationship between addition and subtraction; relate the strategy to a written method and explain the reasoning used. | **Unit 7 Lesson 3 Add and Subtract Decimals** **Unit 7 Lesson 4 Multiply and Divide Decimals by a 1-Digit Whole Number** | **TB 5B:** 17–23, 28–35, 40–52 | **WB 5B:** 9–13, 17–22, 29–39 |

| Common Core State Standards | | Unit | Student Textbook Lessons | Student Workbook Exercises |
|---|---|---|---|---|
| | | Unit 7 Lesson 5 Multiplication by Tens, Hundreds or Thousands | | |
| | | Unit 7 Lesson 6 Division by Tens, Hundreds or Thousands | | |
| | | Unit 8 Lesson 1 Multiplication by a 2-Digit Whole Number | | |
| | | Unit 8 Lesson 2 Division by a 2-Digit Whole Number | | |
| | | Unit 8 Lesson 3 Multiplication by a Decimal | | |
| | | Unit 8 Lesson 4 Division by a Decimal | | |
| **NUMBER AND OPERATIONS – FRACTIONS** | | | | |
| **Use equivalent fractions as a strategy to add and subtract fractions.** | | | | |
| 5.NF.1 | Add and subtract fractions with unlike denominators (including mixed numbers) by replacing given fractions with equivalent fractions in such a way as to produce an equivalent sum or difference of fractions with like denominators. *For example,* $\frac{2}{3} + \frac{5}{4} = \frac{8}{12} + \frac{15}{12} = \frac{23}{12}$. *(In general,* $\frac{a}{b} + \frac{c}{d} = \frac{(ad + bc)}{bd}$ *.)* | Unit 3 Lesson 3 Addition and Subtraction of Unlike Fractions<br><br>Unit 3 Lesson 4 Addition and Subtraction of Mixed Numbers | **TB 5A:** 67–74 | **WB 5A:** 69–76 |

| Common Core State Standards | | Unit | Student Textbook Lessons | Student Workbook Exercises |
|---|---|---|---|---|
| 5.NF.2 | Solve word problems involving addition and subtraction of fractions referring to the same whole, including cases of unlike denominators, e.g., by using visual fraction models or equations to represent the problem. Use benchmark fractions and number sense of fractions to estimate mentally and assess the reasonableness of answers. *For example, recognize an incorrect result $\frac{2}{5} + \frac{1}{2} = \frac{3}{7}$, by observing that $\frac{3}{7} < \frac{1}{2}$.* | **Unit 3 Lesson 3 Addition and Subtraction of Unlike Fractions** <br><br> **Unit 3 Lesson 4 Addition and Subtraction of Mixed Numbers** | **TB 5A:** 75–76 | **WB 5A:** 77–79 |
| **Apply and extend previous understandings of multiplication and division.** | | | | |
| 5.NF.3 | Interpret a fraction as division of the numerator by the denominator $\left(\frac{a}{b} = a \div b\right)$. Solve word problems involving division of whole numbers leading to answers in the form of fractions or mixed numbers, e.g., by using visual fraction models or equations to represent the problem. *For example, interpret $\frac{3}{4}$ as the result of dividing 3 by 4, noting that $\frac{3}{4}$ multiplied by 4 equals 3, and that when 3 wholes are shared equally among 4 people each person has a share of size $\frac{3}{4}$. If 9 people want to share a 50-pound sack of rice equally by weight, how many pounds of rice should each person get? Between what two whole numbers does your answer lie?* | **Unit 3 Lesson 2 Fractions and Division** <br><br> **Unit 3 Lesson 4 Addition and Subtraction of Mixed Numbers** | **TB 5A:** 63–66, 72–76 | **WB 5A:** 66–68, 73–79 |
| 5.NF.4a | Apply and extend previous understandings of multiplication to multiply a fraction or whole number by a fraction. Interpret the product $\left(\frac{a}{b}\right) \times q$ as a parts of a partition of $q$ into $b$ equal parts; equivalently, as the result of a sequence of operations $a \times q \div b$. *For example, use a visual fraction model to show $\left(\frac{2}{3}\right) \times 4 = \frac{8}{3}$, and create a story context for this equation. Do the same with $\left(\frac{2}{3}\right) \times \left(\frac{4}{5}\right) = \frac{8}{15}$. (In general, $\left(\frac{a}{b}\right) \times \left(\frac{c}{d}\right) = \frac{ac}{bd}$.)* | **Unit 4 Lesson 1 Product of Fractions** | **TB 5A:** 91–94 | **WB 5A:** 97–101 |

| Common Core State Standards | | Unit | Student Textbook Lessons | Student Workbook Exercises |
| --- | --- | --- | --- | --- |
| 5.NF.4b | Apply and extend previous understandings of multiplication to multiply a fraction or whole number by a fraction. Find the area of a rectangle with fractional side lengths by tiling it with unit squares of the appropriate unit fraction side lengths, and show that the area is the same as would be found by multiplying the side lengths. Multiply fractional side lengths to find areas of rectangles, and represent fraction products as rectangular areas. | **Unit 5**<br>**Lesson 1**<br>**Square Units** | **TB 5A:**<br>126–128 | **WB 5A:**<br>139–140 |
| 5.NF.5a | Interpret multiplication as scaling (resizing), by: Comparing the size of a product to the size of one factor on the basis of the size of the other factor, without performing the indicated multiplication. | **Unit 4**<br>**Lesson 5**<br>**Product of a**<br>**Fraction and**<br>**Whole Number** | **TB 5A:**<br>77–78, 83 | **WB 5A:**<br>80–81,<br>85–86 |
| 5.NF.5b | Interpret multiplication as scaling (resizing), by: Explaining why multiplying a given number by a fraction greater than 1 results in a product greater than the given number (recognizing multiplication by whole numbers greater than 1 as a familiar case); explaining why multiplying a given number by a fraction less than 1 results in a product smaller than the given number; and relating the principle of fraction equivalence $\frac{a}{b} = \frac{(n \times a)}{(n \times b)}$ to the effect of multiplying $\frac{a}{b}$ by 1. | **Unit 4**<br>**Lesson 5**<br>**Product of a**<br>**Fraction and**<br>**Whole Number** | **TB 5A:**<br>98 | **WB 5A:**<br>106–109 |
| 5.NF.6 | Solve real world problems involving multiplication of fractions and mixed numbers, e.g., by using visual fraction models or equations to represent the problem. | **Unit 3**<br>**Lesson 6**<br>**Word**<br>**Problems** | **TB 5A:**<br>85–87 | **WB 5A:**<br>87–91 |
| 5.NF.7a | Apply and extend previous understandings of division to divide unit fractions by whole numbers and whole numbers by unit fractions. Interpret division of a unit fraction by a non-zero whole number, and compute such quotients. *For example, create a story context for $\left(\frac{1}{3}\right) \div 4$, and use a visual fraction model to show the quotient. Use the relationship between multiplication and division to explain that $\left(\frac{1}{3}\right) \div 4 = \frac{1}{12}$ because $\left(\frac{1}{12}\right) \times 4 = \frac{1}{3}$.* | **Unit 4**<br>**Lesson 3**<br>**Dividing a**<br>**Fraction by a**<br>**Whole Number** | **TB 5A:**<br>99–102 | **WB 5A:**<br>110–116 |

| Common Core State Standards | | Unit | Student Textbook Lessons | Student Workbook Exercises |
|---|---|---|---|---|
| 5.NF.7b | Apply and extend previous understandings of division to divide unit fractions by whole numbers and whole numbers by unit fractions. Interpret division of a whole number by a unit fraction, and compute such quotients. *For example, create a story context for $4 \div \left(\frac{1}{5}\right)$, and use a visual fraction model to show the quotient. Use the relationship between multiplication and division to explain that $4 \div \left(\frac{1}{5}\right) = 20$ because $20 \times \left(\frac{1}{5}\right) = 4$.* | **Unit 4 Lesson 4 Dividing by a Fraction** | **TB 5A:** 103–111 | **WB 5A:** 117–122 |
| 5.NF.7c | Apply and extend previous understandings of division to divide unit fractions by whole numbers and whole numbers by unit fractions. Solve real world problems involving division of unit fractions by non-zero whole numbers and division of whole numbers by unit fractions, e.g., by using visual fraction models and equations to represent the problem. *For example, how much chocolate will each person get if 3 people share $\frac{1}{2}$ lb of chocolate equally? How many $\frac{1}{3}$-cup servings are in 2 cups of raisins?* | **Unit 4 Lesson 4 Dividing by a Fraction** <br><br> **Unit 4 Lesson 5 More Word Problems** | **TB 5A:** 108, 113 | **WB 5A:** 121, 123–127 |
| **MEASUREMENT AND DATA** | | | | |
| **Convert like measurement units within a given measurement system.** | | | | |
| 5.MD.1 | Convert among different-sized standard measurement units within a given measurement system (e.g., convert 5 cm to 0.05 m), and use these conversions in solving multi-step, real world problems. | **Unit 8 Lesson 5 Conversion of Measures** | **TB 5B:** 53–56 | **WB 5B:** 41–42 |
| **Represent and interpret data.** | | | | |
| 5.MD.2 | Make a line plot to display a data set of measurements in fractions of a unit $\left(\frac{1}{2}, \frac{1}{4}, \frac{1}{8}\right)$. Use operations on fractions for this grade to solve problems involving information presented in line plots. *For example, given different measurements of liquid in identical beakers, find the amount of liquid each beaker would contain if the total amount in all the beakers were redistributed equally.* | **Unit 10 Lesson 2 Line Plots** | **TB 5B:** 89–90 | **WB 5B:** 73–74 |

| Common Core State Standards | | Unit | Student Textbook Lessons | Student Workbook Exercises |
|---|---|---|---|---|
| **Geometric measurement: understand concepts of volume.** | | | | |
| 5.MD.3a | Recognize volume as an attribute of solid figures and understand concepts of volume measurement. A cube with side length 1 unit, called a "unit cube," is said to have "one cubic unit" of volume, and can be used to measure volume. | **Unit 9 Lesson 1 Cubic Units** | **TB 5B:** 63 | **WB 5B:** 46–48 |
| 5.MD.3b | Recognize volume as an attribute of solid figures and understand concepts of volume measurement. A solid figure which can be packed without gaps or overlaps using *n* unit cubes is said to have a volume of *n* cubic units. | **Unit 9 Lesson 1 Cubic Units** | **TB 5B:** 63 | **WB 5B:** 46–48 |
| 5.MD.4 | Measure volumes by counting unit cubes, using cubic cm, cubic in, cubic ft, and improvised units. | **Unit 9 Lesson 1 Cubic Units** | **TB 5B:** 64 | **WB 5B:** 46–48 |
| 5.MD.5a | Relate volume to the operations of multiplication and addition and solve real world and mathematical problems involving volume. Find the volume of a right rectangular prism with whole-number side lengths by packing it with unit cubes, and show that the volume is the same as would be found by multiplying the edge lengths, equivalently by multiplying the height by the area of the base. Represent threefold whole-number products as volumes, e.g., to represent the associative property of multiplication. | **Unit 9 Lesson 2 Volume of Rectangular Prisms** | **TB 5B:** 65 | **WB 5B:** 49 |
| 5.MD.5b | Relate volume to the operations of multiplication and addition and solve real world and mathematical problems involving volume. Apply the formulas $V = l \times w \times h$ and $V = b \times h$ for rectangular prisms to find volumes of right rectangular prisms with whole-number edge lengths in the context of solving real world and mathematical problems. | **Unit 9 Lesson 2 Volume of Rectangular Prisms** **Unit 9 Lesson 3 Finding the Volume of a Solid** | **TB 5B:** 65–68, 72–78 | **WB 5B:** 49–50, 54–60 |

| Common Core State Standards | | Unit | Student Textbook Lessons | Student Workbook Exercises |
|---|---|---|---|---|
| 5.MD.5c | Relate volume to the operations of multiplication and addition and solve real world and mathematical problems involving volume. Recognize volume as additive. Find volumes of solid figures composed of two non-overlapping right rectangular prisms by adding the volumes of the non-overlapping parts, applying this technique to solve real world problems. | **Unit 9 Lesson 2 Volume of Rectangular Prisms** | **TB 5B:** 69–71 | **WB 5B:** 51–53 |
| **GEOMETRY** | | | | |
| **Graph points on the coordinate plane to solve real-world and mathematical problems.** | | | | |
| 5.G.1 | Use a pair of perpendicular number lines, called axes, to define a coordinate system, with the intersection of the lines (the origin) arranged to coincide with the 0 on each line and a given point in the plane located by using an ordered pair of numbers, called its coordinates. Understand that the first number indicates how far to travel from the origin in the direction of one axis, and the second number indicates how far to travel in the direction of the second axis, with the convention that the names of the two axes and the coordinates correspond (e.g., $x$-axis and $x$-coordinate, $y$-axis and $y$-coordinate). | **Unit 10 Lesson 3 Coordinate Graphs** | **TB 5B:** 92–95 | **WB 5B:** 75–77 |
| 5.G.2 | Represent real world and mathematical problems by graphing points in the first quadrant of the coordinate plane, and interpret coordinate values of points in the context of the situation. | **Unit 10 Lesson 3 Coordinate Graphs** | **TB 5B:** 102–105 | **WB 5B:** 84–89 |
| **Classify two-dimensional figures into categories based on their properties.** | | | | |
| 5.G.3 | Understand that attributes belonging to a category of two-dimensional figures also belong to all subcategories of that category. For example, all rectangles have four right angles and squares are rectangles, so all squares have four right angles. | **Unit 11 Lesson 1 Looking Back** | **TB 5B:** 117–118 | **WB 5B:** 102–104 |
| 5.G.4 | Classify two-dimensional figures in a hierarchy based on properties. | **Unit 11 Lesson 1 Looking Back** | **TB 5B:** 119 | **WB 5B:** 102–104 |

# Index